*Hope* IN THE EAST
The Mission to Ceylon

# *Hope*
## IN THE EAST
## The Mission to Ceylon

## WILLIAM B. WALSH, M.D.

*New York*
E. P. DUTTON & CO., INC.
*1970*

Dedicated to the memory of the late Dwight David Eisenhower, without whose confidence and faith there would be no HOPE.

# PROLOGUE

"Hope is the dream of a waking man. We live in a waking world, and help give to others the possibility of fulfilling their dreams because we believe in one another."

—Diogenes

By 1968 HOPE had become a symbol throughout the world. It represented much that was good in the American people, and, since its launching eight years before, men and women from fifty states had carried the message of HOPE to four continents.

Her star had risen in the East with that first mission of teaching and training to the Republic of Indonesia. Now for the first time in almost a decade she was to return to the East once again, to the Republic of Ceylon.

From a humble beginning of $150 and the faith of two friends and colleagues—Mr. Joseph T. Geuting, Jr., and the Honorable Eugene M. Zuckert, both of Washington—HOPE had been brought to four continents. The confidence of the late President Dwight D. Eisenhower, who in late 1958 gave me the opportunity to join in the People-to-People Program as cochairman of the Committee on Medicine and Health, had been justified— confidence not in me but rather confidence in his own concept that peace and understanding could best be achieved by the voluntary action of people working together for the betterment of mankind; working together because they chose to work together, not because their governments were enforcing political alliances; working together so that they could learn not only to help themselves but then to go on to help other men to live a better life.

The *Hope* in its own small way brought this concept to Indonesia, Vietnam, Peru, Ecuador, the Republic of Guinea, Nicaragua, and Colombia. Despite the tragic developments which have become history in some of these countries, the staff of the good ship *Hope* was met with friendship, affection and cooperation by people everywhere. Propagandists representing hostile political philosophies did their utmost to disturb this traditional belief that man is basically good. Their efforts have always been frustrated. We ourselves urged years ago that the path to world peace could be broadened only by more work of this kind and not by armed force. We still believe that peace is possible among man. The work and almost stubborn and selfless dedication of our volunteers and staff may well give us the "hope" that this century, at its beginning dedicated to the betterment of man, may in its last thirty years actually concentrate on the well-being of man instead of his destruction.

With these thoughts in mind, in February 1968 we sailed for Ceylon, half a world away, with a greater degree of confidence than ever before. The country was a new and proud one, although its culture had its birth more than two thousand years before our own country was even discovered. We felt this gap could be bridged. We spoke the same language, and we had been colonies, at almost the same time, of the powerful British empire. All of our early contacts seemed to increase our assurance of a trouble-free year; but, as we have learned in the past and learn again on every new voyage, we must work with people as well as governments, and no authority can speak for every individual involved. Ceylon was to present us with challenges, frustrations and rewards. We found that East was still East and West was still West and that we indeed had much yet to learn from one another.

# ILLUSTRATIONS

Doris Biester
Dr. L. Thompson Bowles
Dr. David Furnas et al.
Dr. and Mrs. Robert Kradjian
Drs. Lucienne Lanson and Richard Webb
Mary Lekas et al.
Drs. Hugh Tatlock and Fred E. Gorman
Irene Tegenkamp
Dr. and Mrs. Barry Panter
Dr. Walsh
Elizabeth Brannon

FOLLOWING PAGE 96
Dr. Earl Boehme
Grace Tucker
Dr. Gilbert Mueller, Jr.
Iron Cow
Child drinking milk
Mo Gallagher and Inge Hansen
Mary Louise Foltz
Dr. Henry Bodner
Mary Lou Roppe
Diana Stafford
Dr. Jo Ann Cornet
Vivian Crosswhite
Hungry boy
Sleeping man
Leprosy ward
George White
Dave Godley
Judy Berner
Mrs. Walsh and Bill McDiarmid
Judy Golbuff
Dr. John R. Paul and Patrick McGreal
John Walsh
Peggy Emrey
John Baker
Nancy Brandes

# CHAPTER I

It will be decades before America forgets the spring of 1968: the hopelessness of the war in Vietnam, dissatisfaction with our top leadership, student riots, and finally the first of the year's assassinations. Martin Luther King was dead and Washington was burning!

In those early April days, it seemed as if all the hatreds of hell had engulfed us. The burnings and riotings spread from one end of our country to the other in an insane climax to years of frustration. Reaction to the assassination was not confined to our own continent: there were flag burnings and demonstrations against our embassies and our people everywhere in the world.

It was in this atmosphere that the few of us who were to be the advance unit of *Hope*—the ship that represented so much that was good in America—arrived in Colombo, Ceylon. The left-wing press was thundering against America's "raw savagery," every newspaper to be seen in the crowded streets of this hot and humid city headlined stories of "Yankee assassins." The land of the astrologer, the elephant and the sapphire—"The Resplendent Land" of the travelogues—was not enjoying "Look Toward the West Week" at all.

The Ceylonese Left had been provided with an opportunity

beyond expectation and its press seized the chance to turn from Ceylon's own problems—racial and other—to concentrate on heartless America. (During the year we would learn to cope with this ability to reason by two standards, for the Ceylonese are people who shake their heads in a negative fashion from side to side as they say "right-right" or "yes" in reply to an order or question. There was no major language barrier in this English-speaking country, or so we had been told, but comprehension barriers—yes!)

A commonplace accusation was that the war in Vietnam was being prolonged in order to eliminate our black citizens as well as the brown or yellow people of Asia. Ceylon's own racial problem with the dark-skinned Tamil was overlooked, as were incidents of antiblack prejudice in Russia, Czechoslovakia, Bulgaria, and China. Also buried were memories of persecution in India of the dark-skinned Indian, and the riots pitting the black riverine people of Mauritania against the lighter-skinned ruling Maures. America, and America alone, was to be the sacrificial lamb of the season. Our tremendous strides forward within our system were rarely if every mentioned; even in the polite society of the smile and the limp handshake, we were made to realize that we were not a country of hope but of despair. Behind everything was the feeling against the war in Vietnam. The rightness or wrongness of our position was seldom even considered, only the fact that we, a powerful—the most powerful—nation in the world, were killing Asians.

Why, therefore, was it not as easy for us to embark on a vendetta that would eliminate all of our underprivileged? Some felt the King assassination and the burnings that followed would initiate the end of America. This was the same America to whom every nation of the East looked for help. The same America whose gifts of wheat had enabled Mother India to survive year after year. The same America who had saved Asia from slavery only twenty-five years before. The same America whose pressure and prestige had motivated our allies and friends to give the people of all of Asia their freedom. Memories are almost as short in the East as in some elements of our own society at home. The Ceylonese Ambassador in Washington had urged me not to discuss Vietnam in his country, yet it was a question asked as frequently as what is the *Hope?*

For the past year I had been explaining HOPE to a variety of government officials in Ceylon and to as many of their physicians and surgeons as possible. The air trip halfway around the world had become almost a commuter flight to me, its purpose always to explain, to clarify and to learn to understand the Ceylonese people who had invited us to come to their country to help them.

The Hospital Ship *Hope* and its staff of splendid Americans goes only to those countries that have invited it. Ceylon was to be the eighth nation selected from among the more than thirty invitations extended to us for the year 1968. Successful missions had already been achieved in Indonesia, Vietnam (before the decision was made for a military commitment), Peru, Ecuador, the Republic of Guinea in West Africa, Nicaragua, and Colombia. In several of these nations our teachers continue to work with the many friends who have determined to help themselves by learning and doing.

Ever sensitive to the pride of the newly independent nations and their people, it has always been our policy to go only where we are wanted. We work together as partners with our host nation, each nation expected to bear a part of the cost of the mission. The major part of our costs is borne by private donations. Only a differential subsidy for the cost of our seamen is contributed by our government. Such subsidies are common among almost all ships flying our flag that ply the international waters. Our seamen are the highest paid but provide the finest performance. Our maritime unions have cooperated by agreeing to specialized contracts so that the *Hope's* costs will remain low.

Ours is a mission of mercy in the deepest meaning of that oft-maligned word. We do not go to a nation promising to make all of its blind see, or all of its lame walk. We go to teach and train the local population to take care of themselves. Self-help is the key. At the most qualified professional level we carry out an educational exchange on a doctor-to-doctor basis. At other levels of the medical team—from nurses to sanitary workers, from technicians to secretaries—we teach and teach. It is a twenty-four-hour-a-day task, for when the formal working hours of the day are over, the same interchange takes place at dinner, over cocktails or perhaps at a weekend on the beach. The questions never ended, the answers could not always be found. Not for the first time, we became aware that cultures never fully blend and pride frequently increases prejudice; those without confidence become suspicious, for their own security seems to be threatened by those with greater knowledge.

Many of the blind in Ceylon did not see because of congenital defects, injury and disease. A greater number did not see because there were not enough trained physicians to treat them. The lame and halt in many instances crawled instead of walked for the same reasons. The leper was clapped into his hospital after a quick diagnosis, and little was done afterward to return him to society. The deaf and the dumb were the charge of a dedicated few, but were looked upon as cursed by many, and therefore ignored.

Most pitiful were the thousands who waited for care that was never to be made available because of a rigid and antiquated system of socialized medicine, patterned on the British system, but with modifications peculiar to this island system alone. Men with superb medical skills perform surgery only twelve hours weekly in Ceylon because the government must provide employment to as many physicians as possible. Even though thousands of patients await care, graduate physicians are neither employed nor promised employment because of a lack of priority in the budget. Even if they were to go into practice on their own, they would be denied permission to hospitalize their patients. If an American surgeon were to work only twelve hours weekly he would starve to death. The government still sends students abroad for their training—to Russia, the United States, and other nations—but paradoxically does not recognize their credentials when they return, because only British credentials carry any weight. Members of the hierarchy that controls medical practice all have such credentials, and their quality of mercy is severely tempered by their desire to avoid competition at any cost. In a socialized system (allowing a small amount of private practice on the side), this paradox of private enterprise and its rewards adds to the schizophrenia of the culture of an emerging independent nation.

Not the least of our problems was the support given to the Ayurvedic physician. They are the traditional herb doctors in whom many Ceylonese sincerely believe. Their ministrations are not all bad; their hospital is the cleanest and best managed in the country. They will surely become the Ceylonese psychiatrists of the future, for they perform cures and relieve symptoms by knowing how to persuade a patient to cope with his psychological problems.

Add to this the belief of many that everything from illness to infertility is the result of some evil spirit and one begins to recognize the problems with which we were faced. During my first visit to Ceylon, I thanked my God to find that the bulk of its people spoke English. Then I was advised that as a further blow against Westernization, English had been eliminated from the schools and the traditional language of Sinhalese substituted. This made things not only difficult for us but even for many educated Ceylonese who were to be forced to pass an examination in their "native" tongue, which many of them spoke only slightly. The penalty for failure to pass was to be discharged from the government service. This was also intended to solve their own racial problem, since the Hindu Tamil not only could not speak Sinhala but would, in great numbers, refuse to learn this first language of the Buddhist majority. The plan was to deport the holdouts to India—a type of Ceylonese population control that violated no moral, religious or political concept. Unfortunately it would also result in the loss of the leading businessmen and the hardest workers of the nation, those who kept the tea plantations in production, but such shortsightedness is part of the mystique that is Ceylon.

I could not help but ask during an early visit to that beautiful and confused country, "When you all speak only Sinhalese, with whom else will you speak?" There is an implicit belief that Buddha will watch over all.

The invitation to consider Ceylon as a site for a HOPE mission had been pressed upon me by the dignified and friendly Ceylonese Ambassador to Washington. Acting on behalf of his government and the members of the medical, dental and allied professions, he had been most persuasive. The need was there. An essential basic cadre of trained personnel was available as a nucleus with which we could develop a program, and it seemed that Ceylon felt the need to learn American methods of scientific education.

An additional attraction was that for the first time we felt there would be a minimal language barrier. For eight years we had successfully worked with and trained men and women of different cultures and strange languages. What a pleasure it would be to communicate easily, for the professional people in Ceylon had all been trained in English—before the recent language restrictions had been imposed. The Ambassador, Oliver Weerasinghe, was convincing, and I agreed to visit Colombo to make an on-site appraisal.

Since the war when I had been first exposed to its people, I have always loved Asia. (The war to which I refer is what my generation calls "our war," World War II. What a pity that we identify ourselves in such a fashion.) This affection had been increased by our experience in Indonesia and Vietnam in the early sixties. I still shudder at the nightmare of what has happened in both of those countries since that time, for we worked with thousands of those gentle people. Unfortunately, horror begets horror and violence feeds upon violence, a lesson we ourselves should remember in our own country. In those days many of us pleaded for a new direction in Washington, one directed toward people instead of things. It is sometimes difficult for those who live in a pluralistic society, in which so much depends on material things, to find that it is impossible to transfer this culture or standard to people who are content with so much less.

It was in this same frame of mind that I visited Ceylon. It is not naive to believe that each of us wishes to help himself. It is not impractical to believe that man can only survive by helping his fellow to help himself. It is, in fact, the most pragmatic of all our philosophies. I was not prepared, however, to be received quite as cordially as I was. Never had anyone been showered with so much kindness or courtesy before. Never had there been more complete agreement on both philosophy and ground rules. Never had there been more negative headshaking as we found ourselves in agreement.

This atmosphere was to prevail later when our medical survey and planning units returned to Colombo. Agreements and understandings were reached with the government, the dean of the medical school, individual members of the faculty and physicians in general. Our activities were to be concentrated in two areas, Colombo—the capital city and seat of the older medical school—and in Kandy, the revered city in the mountains of Ceylon, protector of the famed Temple of the Tooth and, more significant to us, the home of a new medical school.

Our training program was to reach every level, from the professors at the school who, in their position as counterparts to ourselves, would work with us to expose house officers (what we call "residents") and medical students to American methods of teaching. Nurses, technologists and auxiliary workers of every type were to be trained. The absorption of those trained into the health economy of the country was agreed upon. No question was raised as to our lack of British qualifications, and all of us looked forward with great anticipation to the coming experience. The Ceylonese were so kind that none of us was sufficiently perceptive to understand the insecurity and uncertainty that lay behind the smiles.

The Permanent Secretary of the Ministry of Health was a Tamil named Balasingham, an imposing man with a smile that lit up his entire face and hair as snowy white as his skin was dark. If only he had had the authority to go with his good sense many of our later trials might well have been avoided. He was our contact point, but unfortunately he was approximately sixth from the top in the bureaucratic chain of command and sixth from the bottom in the health ministry. Socialized medicine as adopted from Ceylon's immediate postwar British masters—a trained civil service—rivaled any bureaucracy in the world. Little did we realize that any agreement had to be confirmed at a number of levels, and there was no such thing as the majority rule of democracy. Each individual through whose hands a piece of paper passed was privileged to veto it or return it to its origin for clarification. Whenever I hear our English cousins lament the dissolution of the Empire, I cannot help but believe that they experience a considerable pleasure in leaving these problems behind. Training is one thing, but the ability to put training to use is quite another cup of tea.

Balasingham never stopped trying, nor did he ever stop smiling. "Anything that you wish, Doctor, we will do for you. You are here to help us," he would say, always shaking his head from left to right. He was able to arrange meetings upon a moment's notice with anyone from the Prime Minister through the entire cabinet and on through every branch of the body politic and the medical fraternity. He understood the strange pride of the medical fraternity, the maneuverings of the politicians. No one ever said no to him, but woe to us who believed that his authority went further than this.

Moreover he had great respect still for the Ayurvedic physician and his medicine; and as a result money was channeled to them in substantial amounts and away from the Western-oriented healer. Perhaps he was correct, for in this land of Buddha, all depended upon the auspicious time and the state of mind. Most patients consulted the astrologer before surgery or any other major undertaking. Is there any doubt that we of the *Hope* must be the world's greatest optimists?

Without any preordained plan, I was in Colombo awaiting the arrival of the ship on April 13, the dawn of the Buddhist and Hindu New Year. She was to arrive the next day, sailing from the south (a most auspicious direction). I was to be dressed in a blue suit, for blue had been determined to be the lucky color for the New Year. Things could not have been more promising. When the rain began to fall we were told these were tears of joy from heaven above. With all of these good signs we couldn't fail, and I'm certain the Christian Lord would have forgiven a momentary thought of conversion to Buddhism. Unfortunately, not being true believers in the mysteries of the stars, neither I nor *Hope*'s staff was to be fully blessed with a trouble-free year.

# CHAPTER 2

What is "The Resplendent Land," the emerald isle of the Indian Ocean, toward which the *Hope* was heading? The entire nation of Ceylon occupies only slightly more than twenty-five thousand square miles of the Indian Ocean off the southeastern tip of India. It is only two hundred and seventy miles long and on a map looks like a knotty pear suspended from a tree. Approximately the size of West Virginia, it cradles fourteen million people who, if they continue to multiply at present rates, will before long be forced into the very Indian Ocean from whose bottom the land has risen. The vast majority of the people are Sinhalese, with a small percentage of Tamils and a variety of other citizens, the result of multiple occupations by the Portuguese, the Dutch, and the British. A virtual one-product country—second only to India in its production of tea—Ceylon seems to be rushing headlong into the seventeenth century with import and export restrictions that defy development of other products.

A land of sapphires and other gems, a nation whose wealth was coveted by others for years, its hard currency now flows to Swiss banks through the ingenuity of the gem merchants. It is a land of unexcelled pageantry, contrasts of the greenest of jungles and the most arid of all ground—brown and dry—unbelievably hot. A sign of wealth and comfort is the ownership of an elephant or a pair of bullocks. It is said that it takes fifteen years to train an elephant and that he is then worth about four thousand dollars, for he will work forever and feeds only from the gifts of the land around him. But to those of us who come from a different world the patience of the Ceylonese to wait for the future to come to him can be a cause for consternation.

Ceylon became an independent member of the British Commonwealth in 1948 and proclaimed Sinhalese the official language in 1956; this led to bloody riots shortly thereafter and intensified the disease of nationalism which has retarded Ceylon's development ever since. No man is an expert on the problems of another nation, particularly after only a few brief years of exposure to its people. However, I confess my amazement on hearing the remark of a government official upon his return from a Commonwealth Conference in early 1969. He, in turn, had been amazed to find that the conference, attended by more than twenty nations, had been conducted in English! He was deadly serious.

Prime Minister Dudley Senanayake himself embodies the contrasts that are Ceylon. A kind man and a religious Buddhist, he was educated in Great Britain and became an ardent golfer and a lover of apples, which Ceylon is no longer permitted to import. The gift from us he most appreciated was an occasional bag of apples from the ample refrigerated hold of the *Hope*. We, because of the nature of our mission, were free of import restrictions for all items necessary for the fulfillment of our objectives. The joy of the Prime Minister at our periodic "Johnny Appleseed" gesture was an important part of the international cooperation so necessary to our work.

The tale of the apple and its former place in Ceylon is a simple example of the adherence to British tradition. Because of the old proverb, "An apple a day keeps the doctor away," the Prime Minister explained to me that the apple became the traditional gift for patients in the hospital. There was a constant demand for their importation from Australia, and as rapidly as they were imported they were purchased. In a currency-poor nation, apples became a black-market item after independence and hence the import restriction.

Dudley Senanayake had run for office because of his concern over the destruction of Ceylon's economy by its preceding Communist-dominated government. He made as many as ten speeches a day for the forty days of the campaign. His only sustenance from morning till night was a flask of tea. His greatest sacrifice during the campaign was the abandonment of his daily morning round of golf—a sport which he believes in almost as strongly as he does his Buddhist religious principles. The man who has outlawed alcoholic beverages at official functions because of those religious beliefs is a westernized golf addict of the most fervent variety. The man who believes in the necessity of a Sinhalese national language still treasures an occasional Western apple. These contrasts represent the Ceylon I had been visiting for the past year and to which *Hope* was now committed.

# CHAPTER 3

Aboard the *Hope,* anticipation had overtaken the boredom that ultimately sets in after forty days at sea. The crossing, which had begun on a rainy afternoon in Philadelphia, was not without its excitement, sadness and consternation, but *Hope* is far from a cruise ship and the hundred and twenty-five members of our permanent hospital staff are crammed into every conceivable space. Her crew of ninety-two spend their sailing time completing work that is never quite finished in the shipyard overhaul, and sail the ship as well.

Weather was bad between Philadelphia and Fort Lauderdale, where a brief visit was scheduled. The Dramamine was in great demand, and many of the first-timers on our staff were already pondering the wisdom of their decision to come. The old-timers, like all old salts, pretended to feel no ill effects, although they too seemed to subsist on soda crackers and consommé rather than the regular fare.

At Fort Lauderdale, Harry Hatharasinghe, a former Air Ceylon pilot but currently on leave from Pan American, joined the ship to give our staff their first taste of Ceylon, its language and its culture. More than anyone else, he was to make the next forty days bearable. He had volunteered for the task of making our staff love his country and its people before the end of the voyage. On the evening of our departure from Florida, he serenaded us with Ceylonese songs. The romance had begun.

He was a handsome man in his forties with black wavy hair, stocky and brown-skinned. His face was strong and proud, with a firm mouth and square jaw. A complete extrovert of great charm, he was determined that all would understand his Buddhist religion and its customs. It was a foregone conclusion that Sinhalese would be the language of *Hope*, for never was there a more severe teacher. Four days a week, he held class after class in conversational Sinhalese. All tried, some learned. His pièce de résistance was the teaching of the Ceylonese National Anthem "Sri Lanka" to our entire team so that they might sing it for the Prime Minister on the ship's arrival. He was a stringent choirmaster, and many begged for mercy as nightly he demanded, as he clapped his hands together, "Now, once more!"

But there was more than sailing and singing. This was the time for making our hospital ready, finalizing teaching programs and a blending of the old staff with the new. Dorothy Aeschliman, our chief nurse who has been with us ever since *Hope* came on the scene, gave her team not only the usual nurses' duties, but had them also scrubbing, painting, hauling equipment and the like. A spirit was once again being welded, a spirit that year after year makes our nursing staff the envy of all who come into contact with it.

Walt Rogers, our chief of staff, and Bill Peters, our hospital administrator, conducted series of meetings with our permanent medical staff, a small but highly capable group of physicians, who spent their days planning, discussing and, as more physicians do, plain disagreeing on many aspects of our approach to teaching in Ceylon. Two of our specialists—Bob Kradjian, a general surgeon, and Barry Panter, a young pediatrician—were also adjusting to married life. Bob was virtually a newlywed and Barry an old-timer of about a year's duration. Fortunately for us, Chris Kradjian was a superb nurse trained specially in coronary intensive care, a skill totally lacking in Ceylon. Mary Lou Panter was a pediatric nurse and one of *Hope*'s prettiest and most charming. As the astrologer would say, these signs were most auspicious.

Norm and Tysie Sears had joined us after two years in Afghanistan and they, together with Jerry Lawlor, a veteran of past voyages, made up our coordinating medical team. Norm and Jerry were responsible for coordinating the major medical programming on board, so that when our volunteer specialists arrived for their two-month tours they could slide right into a going program.

When we reached Durban on the coast of Africa, the American Consul boarded the ship with the pilot as we entered the South African port to fuel. His job was to explain the ground rules of Apartheid: white passengers were to take cabs driven by white drivers only and stay on their own side of the post office. Don't try to change the world here, it's their country! There were many more restrictions, all harsh, but real. Our Negro staff members remained on board, as did many others. Some, desperately tired of the sea, went ashore to visit the game preserve at Natal's Lion Park, watch the Zulu dances or drive through the Valley of the Thousand Hills. The countryside is beautiful and vast, and, as in our own, the tensions in the hills and the valleys can only be felt, not seen.

April second was the beginning of the end of the tale of one hundred and twenty-five ancient mariners. The pace quickened and spirits began to lift. Then three days later came the news of the assassination of Martin Luther King in Memphis, Tennessee.

As always at sea, there were not many early details and perhaps this was a blessing. Days were to pass before the staff was to hear of the burning, the looting, the madness on the streets— the very violence which Dr. King abhorred. Everyone was stunned and shocked. Many spoke of it, some wrote about it, others simply and quietly reflected. The wiser prayed. Our crew, many of whom were black, at first seemed unable to believe what had happened. Given the violence of the reaction at home it was fortunate that so many had been with us before. There was no resentment, no hate, just a sadness that cannot be described. Many wept as if they had lost someone of their own. Strong, simple and even occasionally selfish men, but on this day they were in mourning as one.

Then news bulletins began to arrive and the details of American rioting were posted all over the ship, and on April 7 a joint memorial service was held with the participation of both of our chaplains and led by George White, a member of our crew.

Now the days passed faster, the water became bluer, and by April 14 Ceylon lay just over the horizon. On Sunday morning wide-winged, beautiful gulls were flying over our ship, whose white sides were marked by those large letters, *Hope*. Shortly we would enter Colombo harbor. The nights of restful sleep on deck would end, the silence of the hospital would be replaced with the busy activities of men and women trying to heal, teach and learn. Our girls were preparing their white uniforms for the next morning, and Harry Hatharasinghe was giving them their last rehearsal of the "Sri Lanka." They sang it perfectly, and he clasped his hands approvingly and bowed his head in the traditional gesture of *abuyovan,* meaning "May your life be a long and happy one."

# CHAPTER 4

As the *Hope* sailed toward its rendezvous with the pilot boat, ready for docking in Colombo, all its staff in dress whites strained to get the look and feel of the land of which they were about to become a part.

None was more nervous than little "Mo" Gallagher. Christened Maureen by her delighted Irish parents in Newport some twenty-five years before, Mo, a *Hope* veteran, was about to embark on another and—it seemed to her—more frightening adventure. She was a small black-haired girl with a very big heart, a great sense of humor and the spirit of one twice as tall. As if to emphasize this she had chosen Dori Biester as her roommate. Dori, at a little better than six feet, was as tall as Mo was short. Redheaded and as beautiful as only a beautiful redhead can be, she and Mo formed quite a team. Both were pediatric nurses and had been with us in Colombia on our previous mission. Each child in the pediatric ward seemed too big for little Mo to fondle or carry, while Dori seemed to lose them in her arms. Both had a tenderness, an aura about them that captured everyone in the ward, parent and child alike.

Shortly after leaving Philadelphia, all the girls—nurses, technicians and secretaries—had had to pack their belongings care-

fully away, for rooms big enough for only one held two and
rooms for two housed three. Our newest girls were packed four
in a room intended for only three and closet and storage space
was at a premium. The old-timers, who could be expected to
know better had brought even more than the new girls, with the
difference that they knew what counted. Still Mo and Dori
didn't really need two record players in their double-bunked
room. After days of moving gear around and deciding that Dori
was simply too tall to sleep in the upper bunk, life had settled
down to routine, and conjecture began at once: who was going
to be sent to the hospital at Kandy?

Seventy miles away from the ship and nestled high in the
mountains, Kandy was the home of a hospital and new medical
school. HOPE had pledged to work there and, in addition to
sending a group of physician specialists, had promised to send
half a dozen nurses and technicians to see what could be done
to change habits and training in the hospital. Until now, Kandy
had been identified only through the *National Geographic Magazine*
or the romantic tales of Harry Hatharasinghe. However,
as the briefing plans for Ceylon unfolded it appeared more and
more "that" place away from ship and friends.

It was in mid-March on a beautiful day at sea that Mo was
called to the office by head nurse Dorothy Aeschliman and told
that she was to be the first nurse from pediatrics to go to Kandy.
Mo was delighted, stunned and nervous all at the same time.
Her freckled face paled, flushed and lit up in an all-encompass-
ing smile as she muttered something—she knows not what—to
Dorothy. As Dorothy gave her instructions and background, it is
doubtful if Mo heard a word. Her thoughts ran to the fear that
always accompanies new challenge. As she heard dimly the
names of others to be assigned with her, she recognized familiar
names, but none was a close friend. Her thoughts ran to the inevitable loneliness, the rains of the monsoon that were due to
hit in the coming weeks and last for months. She knew she
would miss the camaraderie of the ship that meant so much at

the end of a trying day. How good it always was, she thought, to come back to the boat deck lounge at night and find that no matter what had gone wrong during the day, someone else had had it worse. More than that, each could share his little victory and achievement, and nothing contributed more to staff morale.

Now she was to be on her own. Still, she thought, what a wonderful chance to get to know herself. She thought too of her God and silently said "Thy will be done," and took strength in knowing she believed this fervently.

Mumbling a "thanks for your confidence" to Dorothy, she rushed back to her room to tell Dori. The news caused both tears and delight for the girls had grown to be very good friends and already had made many plans. Dori, in her calm manner, gave Mo the reassurance she needed. Anyone who knows this spunky Irish lass realized that the confidence was already there. In no time at all, they had arrived at a name for the group designated to go to Kandy. Forever after they would be known as "the Kandy Kids."

The Kandy Kids were together daily, talking, planning, imagining, for of course none had ever seen the Kandy Hospital. They could not have imagined that, like a tea plantation, it climbed up a mountainside—one ward built on top of another. On foggy mornings, those working in the lab would be unable to see those working in the wards below. But this was their future. Today was arrival—Colombo today, Kandy tomorrow.

The ship was due to dock at eleven on April 15, which was Pre-Poya day. Poya isn't Sunday, but Pre-Poya is just like a Western Saturday. About two years earlier, Ceylon had decided to live by the Buddhist calendar. Pre-Poya days and Poya days depend upon the position of the moon and such days occur at the quarter, half, three-quarter, and full moons. These do not fall necessarily seven days apart, and the result creates havoc when coordinated with the usual Western calendar. We had long since determined that when in Rome we would live as the Romans do, though in truth it almost killed us. It was months before we became accustomed to a routine in which some weeks were four days long while others took nine. I don't believe that the local population was too happy with the return to old ways either, but none dared protest living by the Buddhist calendar.

So we arrived on Pre-Poya Day which meant that until one o'clock in the afternoon everyone had to remain at work. Unfortunately, the tides did not recognize the calendar, be it Buddhist or Western, and we had to come in at eleven. Mo and her cohorts were disappointed at what seemed like a meager welcome; the dock area appeared deserted. They had no way of knowing that the dock workers had been on strike for weeks and felt only the letdown of no greeting after forty days at sea.

A few workers had been given permission to help bring in the *Hope* without fear of being called blacklegs, their British word for strikebreakers. The large and beautiful port was currently glutted with ships. Many had been ready to sail for weeks, but because of the strike could neither discharge nor take on cargo. The leftist-controlled unions were doing all possible to make the life of the government miserable, and we were frankly surprised that they permitted us to dock.

As the *Hope* neared the Queen Elizabeth Quay, the staff caught its first sight of the long shed, surrounded by potted palms, which was to be the site of our official welcome later in the afternoon. A few of the more curious strikers waved as they stood barefooted in their white sarongs. Majestically off the bow appeared a Buddhist temple open to all seafarers who wished to give thanks for the safety of their voyage. There were shouts of joy and recognition from the small welcoming committee composed of our advance unit members and those physician members of the first rotation who had already arrived. Many had served with *Hope* before, so it was a meeting of old friends on foreign soil.

The Kandy Kids had to prepare to move off the ship immediately, taking their luggage and supplies to the Taprobane Hotel.

Not even the excitement of the landing could stop the tears of the half dozen girls who were initially moving only five minutes away. The ship was their home, the staff their family, and the Taprobane and Kandy represented something remote and strange. Their move completed, they returned to the ship by early afternoon, ready for the official welcome to Ceylon which was to be extended by Prime Minister Dudley Senanayake and members of his cabinet.

The local committee had been preparing for days. A large shed about six hundred feet in length had been constructed so as to protect all from either the hot sun or the unpredictable seasonal "tears of joy." All around the shed were potted green palms, their branches waving lazily in the afternoon breeze. A small raised platform had been constructed in the center of the shed so that all seated upon it would be facing the ship. On either side were row upon row of chairs to seat the diplomatic corps and other honored guests. A red carpet led from the platform and along the dock halfway to the outer entrance of the dock area. This, too, was bordered by rows of palms on both sides for the several hundred yards to the entrance of the port itself.

Chief of staff Walter Rogers and I had been instructed to meet the Prime Minister and his party at the gate at exactly three o'clock. The official party was to be preceded to the platform by the famed Kandyan dancers, in full regalia and accompanied by clanging cymbals. They were already warming up at the gate, much like a football team at home before the kickoff. Joints were being stretched and arms twisted in the various graceful motions that were to be a part of the dance. All were males—short, well-muscled men who were accustomed to performing in perfect unison and rhythm the intricate mime movements that made each dance a story. Each dancer seemed to carry a ton of silver ornamentation in breastplates and arm and ankle bracelets. Their only other clothing were turbans and bil-

lowing white pants. Some color was added by the symbolic redness of the teeth and gums of those who were habitual chewers
of the betel nut, the common tranquilizer of Ceylon.

Fortunately the offical party arrived on schedule. Both Walt
Rogers and I were already drenched in perspiration after waiting only a few moments. Then as if by signal the rains began
softly but steadily—the tears of joy which were supposed to be
so auspicious. There was a thunderous clang of cymbals, and
the strange singing voices of the dancers rang through the air.
Slowly and deliberately we began the long walk to the ship.
The Prime Minister, bareheaded and untroubled by the rain, set
the pace which was actually governed by the dancers. They
would dance ahead of us, moving forward, then momentarily
stop and begin again. As we rounded the corner of the gate sep-
arating our dock area from the main part of the entrance, we
saw our staff. Nurses, technicians and secretaries—all in their
starched white uniforms—lined both sides of the red carpet that
had been so carefully laid for the Prime Minister. I shall never
forget that sight, for at that moment they were the most beautiful women in the world. Even His Excellency was startled and
tried to find something appropriate to say.

As we passed them, each clasped her hands together in front
of her chest and bowed her head in that lovely Ceylonese gesture, the *abuyovan*. The Prime Minister returned their thoughtful courtesy, bowing similarly first to the right, then to the left.
The rain meant little, the first recognition of the need for friendship had become apparent. The best was yet to come.

After we ascended the platform, the Ceylon Military Band
played the Ceylonese National Anthem. Our staff had drawn
themselves up in multiple lines before the platform and sang out
loud and clear in perfect Sinhalese. The Prime Minister was so
overwhelmed that silent tears started down his cheeks. He
turned and said, "They sing our anthem better than our own
people." My heart was too full to make a reply.

Colombo harbor where the *Hope* was anchored. (*National Geographic Society*)

RIGHT: Official guests are led to the S.S. *Hope* by Kandyan dancers. BELOW: Nurses from the hospital ship form a guard of honor for the Prime Minister. At left is Harry Hatharasinghe who prepares the nurses to sing the Ceylonese national anthem for the Prime Minister.

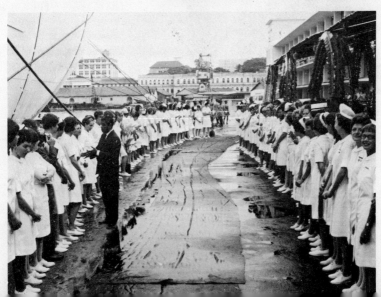

Dorothy Aeschliman (center front), the chief nurse aboard the ship, joins other nurses to sing the Ceylonese national anthem during the welcoming ceremonies.

LEFT, ABOVE: The Prime Minister, Dudley Senanayake, and Mrs. Vimala Kannangara, Junior Minister of Health, are shown through the ship by Dr. Walsh. LEFT, BELOW: Dr. Walter C. Rogers, the chief of the HOPE medical staff, works in his office aboard the hospital ship.

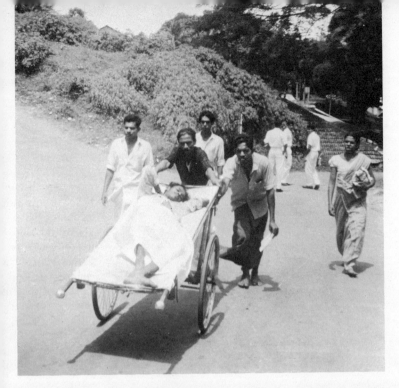

ABOVE: A sick Ceylonese man on a litter is pushed by friends toward the hospital ship. BELOW: Dr. William McCafferty examines a patient in one of the men's wards of the hospital ship. Assisting him is a Ceylonese nurse counterpart.

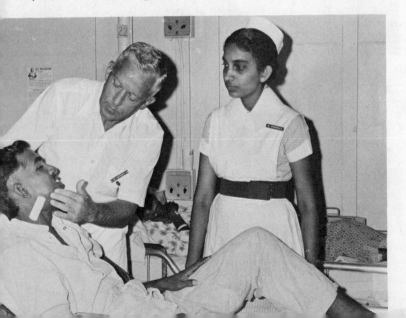

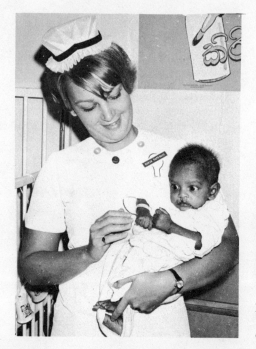

LEFT: Susan Pap[...]
holds Jagath Siri[...]
an infant patient [...]
aboard the ship.
BELOW: A HOPE [...]
Esther Pierce, her [...]
counterpart, and [...]
Ceylonese patient[...]
celebrate Shanti's [...]
birthday. Shanti, [...]
pediatric patient [...]
(right), blows ou[...]
candles on his cak[...]

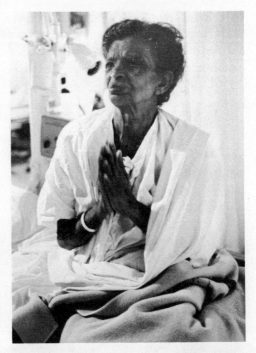

RIGHT: An elderly
patient aboard the
hospital ship prays to
her god, Buddha.
BELOW: Dr. William
Moss, a HOPE surgeon,
talks with a smiling
patient recovering from
surgery.

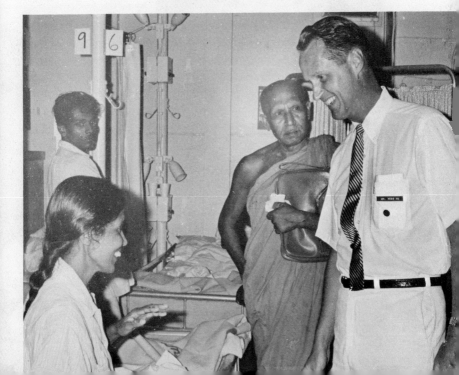

LEFT: Sylvia Lawrence, a HOPE pediatric nurse, and two young patients in the pediatric ward aboard the S.S. *Hope.* BELOW: A HOPE Nursing Educator, Sato Hashizume, and her Ceylonese counterpart teach a class in public health to a group of Ceylonese nurses in the Kresge portable classroom on the deck of the hospital ship.

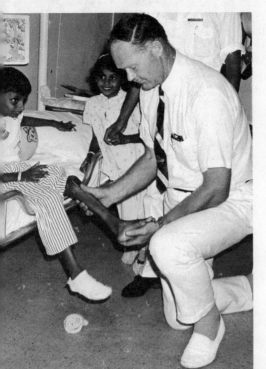

Dr. William T. Hall, an orthopedic surgeon, checks the progress of a young patient in the pediatrics ward aboard the hospital ship.

Physiotherapist Ruth Howard escorts a young patient to the gangway. The boy had polio as a small child and it was only after surgery by Hope doctors and the help of braces that he was taught to walk again.

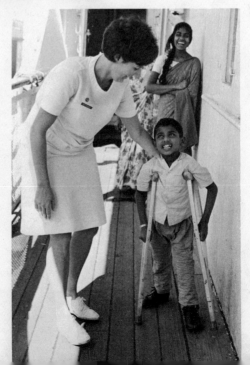

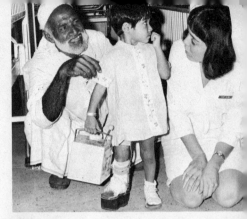

Jenalhulumma, a young patient aboard the hospital ship, visits with her grandfather and a HOPE nurse, Mary Clark.

Joelyn Bymoen and a Ceylonese student nurse enter a portable classroom situated on the deck of the ship.

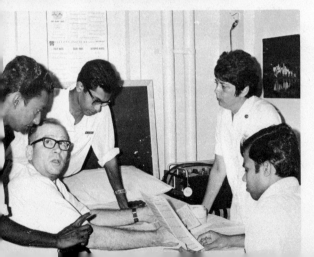

Dr. Owen Beard and Gloria Hammond, an EKG technician, discuss electrocardiograms with Ceylonese students aboard the hospital ship.

Dr. Samuel Kron makes the traditional gesture of greeting to a young pediatric patient aboard the hospital ship.

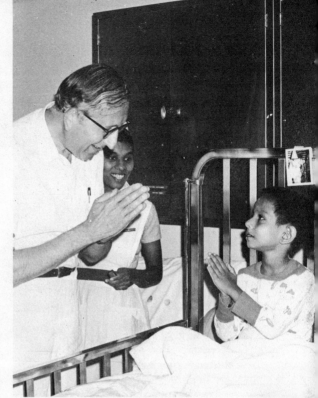

Dr. Mel Foote and his Ceylonese counterpart work side by side in the ENT (eye, nose and throat) clinic.

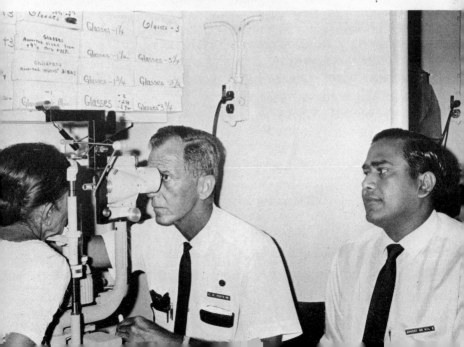

Dr. Robison D. Harley, a HOPE ophthalmologist, examines two young brothers whose sight he was able to restore after delicate eye operations.

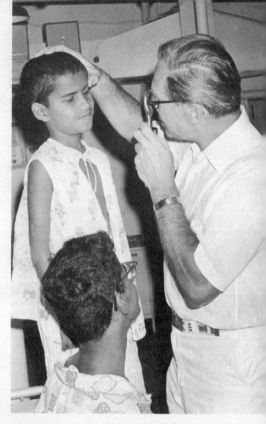

Jeanette Dillman and her surgical supply counterpart prepare sterilized equipment in the sterilizing unit of the hospital ship.

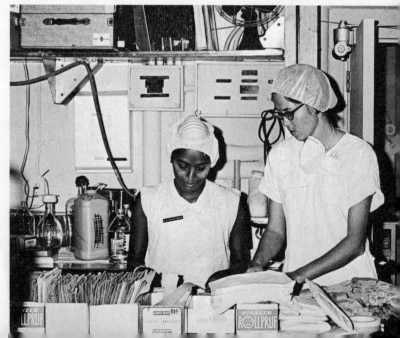

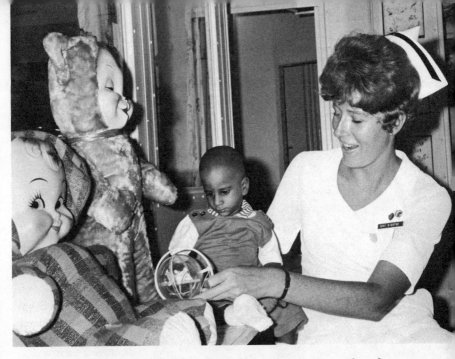

ABOVE: HOPE nurse, Doris Biester, plays with a young patient aboard the hospital ship. Each pediatric patient is given a toy of his own before he leaves the ship. BELOW: Dr. L. Thompson Bowles discusses an X ray of a patient with a radiologist aboard the hospital ship.

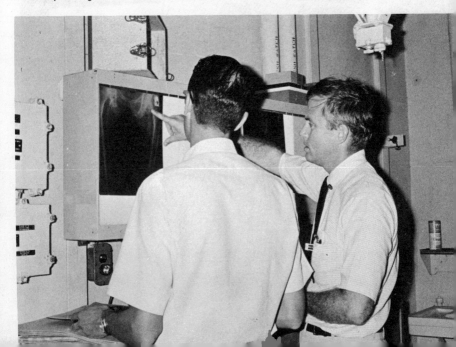

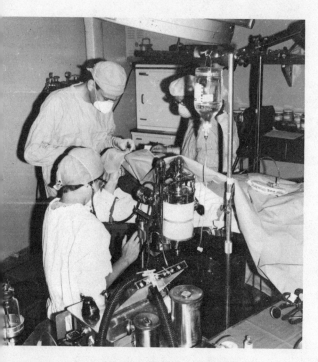

Dr. David Furnas, a HOPE plastic surgeon, is assisted by Connie Blish (front), anesthetist, and Kay Williams, an operating room nurse, in one of the many operations performed on the hospital ship.

A HOPE husband-wife medical team, Dr. and Mrs. Robert Kradjian examine a patient aboard the S.S. *Hope*.

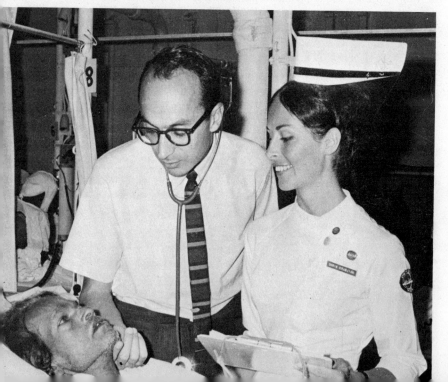

Dr. Lucienne Lanson and Dr. Richard Webb discuss a patient's condition aboard the S.S. *Hope* in Ceylon.

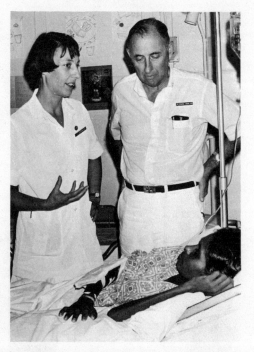

Mary Lekas, a HOPE otolaryngologist, discusses the inner ear with Mary Morris, Annette Hirsch and Ceylonese counterparts.

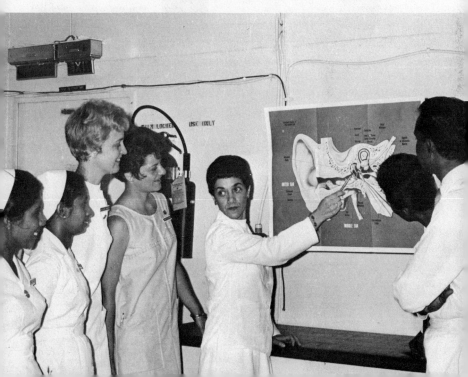

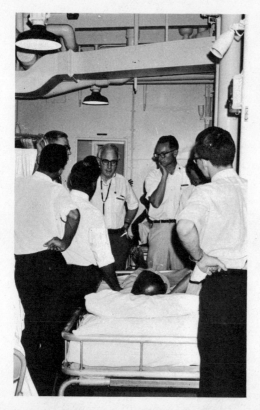

Dr. Hugh Tatlock (left center) and Dr. Fred E. Gorman (right center) discuss a patient's symptoms in one of the wards on the hospital ship.

Irene Tegenkamp confers with one of her cytology technician students.

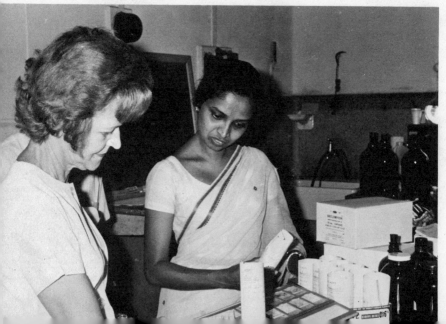

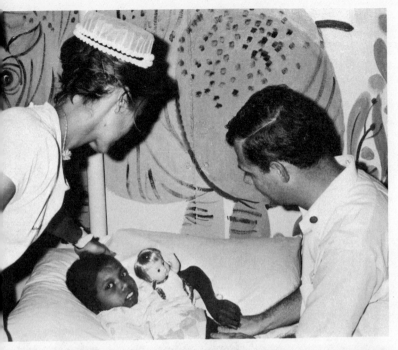

ABOVE: A HOPE husband-wife team, Dr. and Mrs. Barry Panter, talk with Pushpam, a young patient in the pediatrics ward aboard the ship.
BELOW: Dr. Walsh and pediatric patients aboard the hospital ship.

Mr. M. T. J. Wijayasiri, a former patient aboard the hospital ship, presents Elizabeth Brannon, the HOPE nutritionist, a gift of bananas and string beans from his farm.

# CHAPTER 5

The welcoming ceremonies, which had dragged on for hours, were finally at an end. The Prime Minister and his party had left the ship clutching their bags of apples. Kevun, murukku, kiribath and plantains had all been served by charming and beautiful Ceylonese maidens clothed in colorful saris. We dared not refuse even the hottest food. No wonder carcinoma of the esophagus was common in Ceylon! The *Hope* staffers were wondering whether these delicious but highly seasoned Ceylonese specialties would result in the Eastern version of the Aztec two-step.

But now it was time to get on with the business at hand. Reality in this dreamland was already closing in. Those of us in the advance team had become concerned at certain changes we had found. After our initial curriculum had been planned and approved, the Minister of Health was replaced by a man who was not a physician. His was a political appointment, and although this was none of our business, it was certainly some cause for worry. He admittedly knew little about *Hope*, and, unfortunately, even less about the problems of medicine in Ceylon—particularly those in Colombo. He had held high office in Kandy for more than thirty years and was resented by many of the physicians there. He was cordial enough and kind to us, but his kindness had caused a small segment of the physicians in the city of Colombo to resent us.

An additional and unexpected blow was the replacement of the dean of the medical school. Our planning at the school had been carried out with Dean Aberatyne, one of Ceylon's most revered and respected teachers. He was an elderly man and according to local tradition would have been respected by all, if only for his age alone. The new dean was young, arrogant, unsure of himself—the insecurity doubtless being the reason for his show of arrogance. Added to this was the fact that he had been the student of several of the proud medical school professors which caused additional difficulties, given the complex Ceylonese culture and its reverence for age. Traditionally unable to exercise authority over his seniors, he was, in his own mind, dean in name only. Our own position was even more shaky since no one had thought to tell us about the new dean.

This lack of communication, which was to plague us throughout the year, is not unusual in Ceylon. It is difficult to pinpoint the blame, for in such a society authority seems to rest in the hands of everyone and yet with no one. It is possible for anyone in the chain of command to resist or halt progress or defer a decision. So many are involved it is never anyone's fault.

The new dean felt we should have contacted him despite the fact that we didn't know of his appointment. He conceded that it was the "stupidity" of someone at the Ministry, but that was certainly not his fault. Therefore we had insulted him, and he was not going to cooperate. The Ministry on the other hand gave themselves complete absolution, but felt that they could not exert too much pressure on the faculty or the physicians without provoking a strike. Striking is one of the privileges of democracy that even the most autocratic states have adopted.

We found ourselves in a position in which we could be easily made to look foolish; it was a situation which bordered on comic opera. Despite all of these problems jeopardizing the vital beginning of our mission, we had been welcomed in public in lavish fashion by the Prime Minister. There had been nation-wide radio and press coverage, and all of the officials of the health ministry and the majority of the faculty members from the university had attended the reception following. Everyone had been friendly; enthusiastic conversations between our faculty and theirs had gone on throughout the afternoon. The first patients selected for admission were to be brought on board the next morning. Serenity was the keynote. But as the sun went down and our conference with the faculty members began, we looked at one another and wondered what madness this was.

One of the characteristics which seems to be a part of each *Hope* team member is a dogged optimism. More than that, each volunteer, permanent or rotating staff member, is with the project not only to fulfill an assignment but to fulfill something within himself. It is an honest need, consciously acknowledged by some and perhaps not realized by others. But a spirit of singular dedication is there, which makes each and all immune to momentary discouragements.

However, on this occasion the shock was somewhat greater than we had ever experienced before. Moreover we had not fully circulated what information we had while en route to Ceylon. Our professional coordinators had not all had a chance to study the voluminous survey material accumulated months earlier. Our coordinators, when faced with the change in the atmosphere in Ceylon, became unsure of their function and of their ability to carry out their responsibilities. It was my job to overcome this defeatism.

A bright note was the completely opposite attitude taken by the nurses and the remainder of our permanent staff. Dorothy Aeschliman's nine years with *Hope* had prepared her for the improbable and impossible. She let nothing stand in her way. Her nurses were fully briefed and beautifully organized. The Director of Nursing Education, hand-picked by Dorothy, had planned probably the finest training program we ever had. Her liaison with our nursing education office in Washington was ideal. This part of our program happily never faltered.

But the nurses did not have the problems which, as chief of staff, Walt Rogers faced. Our preliminary survey indicated that despite the invitation extended by the combined wishes of the government, the university and the medical profession, a small but vocal segment of the local profession would most assuredly obstruct our efforts. The opposition were men in three highly specialized fields of medicine. They were few in number but, because they were the only local men trained in these fields, they had a great deal of power. But even they had indicated grudgingly that if everyone else wanted *Hope's* help, they would go along. I, personally, had both spoken with them and toured their wards earlier in the year as had the members of our professional survey team. The consensus was that these Ceylonese physicians, though highly competent, could profit from our help, but we judged that none but the best America could offer could be sent to work with them. We outlined the needs we recognized and thought we were in agreement with them on the areas in which they would appreciate our assistance. How could Walt, encouraged by this reception and accord, count on anything less than the fulfillment of the expressed intentions? But, suddenly, the atmosphere changed drastically.

The very same men now pretended that the coming of *Hope* had never been discussed with them. The *Hope* staff talked for hours on that evening of our awakening. Since we were by ourselves, it cannot be denied that Walt used some salty expressions in reference to their attitude—not without the concurrence of the rest of us. It was impossible to determine with any degree of certainty the reason for the changed attitude. Most felt it was insecurity, a fear perhaps that the techniques and knowledge of our own specialists would somehow make them seem inferior in the eyes of their colleagues. This was an unnecessary fear, if indeed it was one at all. Our experience had taught us many years earlier, on another continent, that change cannot be imposed. It must be both desired and accepted. Our credo had always been that we are the invited guests in the house of our hosts and we behave accordingly, neither imposing our techniques nor denigrating those of others. Medicine is an international language, and no two physicians can ever sit down in discussion of a subject without learning from each other.

We could not, of course, rule out the possibility that politics lay behind our difficulties, but politics was a field in which we were not expert. We could not permit *Hope* to be used as a tool by either side—the government or the profession—simply to prove a political point. Many of the physicians who were proving inhospitable to us had been appointed during the previous administration of a Communist-dominated government. But whether politically or professionally motivated, these men had skills vital to the success of our mission. We could only conjecture and reassert our faith in *Hope*, and ourselves. We knew that if we began our work despite apparent obstacles, the project would succeed as it always had. The people would know that we were in their country only because we believed in their willingness to help themselves and because we as Americans believed that cause to be worthwhile.

Our decision and dedication reaffirmed, we slept well. We had not bargained, however, for what the left-wing press had in store for us the next day. For those who had seen the wonderful success of the *Hope* in the past in the face of fierce opposition, the outcries were probably no great surprise. But for those who were with us for the first time, the first two weeks in Ceylon could only have been baffling. It was immediately apparent that the Communists in Ceylon could not afford to have the compassion and concern of the American people demonstrated. They wasted no time in launching the "Big Lies."

One typical story was headlined, "This *Hope* Is For Spying." It went on to state: "This ship created political sicknesses wherever it went to. It is a floating spy center . . . they are devils who come to create sickness as a blessing. . . . But modern

Americans are more specialists on their cursed culture than on medical science. What specialists are the doctors on the *Hope?* If they are specialists they need not go adrift in the sea. It is absurd for the *Hope* to go about showing kindness to others without treating the numerous causes of social disease in America itself. . . . Should we not be suspicious when Americans who massacre Buddhists in Vietnam by employing medical science in brutal methods such as germ warfare, come to Ceylon to cure the sick. . . . But American medical science is used for murder also. Can we imagine that such an inhuman and brutal lot can cure us?"

Still another leftist paper charged: "The Yankees who send the Peace Corps to Foreign countries and cause wars have now sent out a new fortress to Ceylon in the name of the Hospital Ship *Hope.* One should be very alert to detect the new epidemics she is to spread in Ceylon."

The biggest lies came in a series of articles simultaneously published in several Communist periodicals which referred to the *Hope* as the "Big Pueblo." They accused us of having huge experimental laboratories below deck, built and equipped by "Fortress Dietrich" in the United States, dedicated to bacteriological warfare research. No matter how often these reporters were invited to tour the "suspected" areas, they declined and then wrote that permission was refused. Each time a *Hope* physician or nurse visited a village or a home by invitation, the left-wing press reported that cameras were carried so as to photograph secret installations, and that specimen bottles were always in hand to preserve bacteria for their experiments in germ warfare. A thousand spies were said to have entered Ceylon within two weeks after our arrival, who were now secreted all over the island.

These and other accusations would have been ridiculous if either the government or the medical association had spoken in our defense. Instead, the lies were ignored. We felt we had to adopt the same policy. A few of the local physicians enlarged the rumors, if they did not start them, by slyly questioning the qualifications of our volunteer specialists. This was simple to do, for, as stated before, Ceylon recognizes officially only British specialty certification.

Ignoring the lies did not eliminate them. It only inspired the leftists to come up with even more outlandish accusations in their effort to discredit the *Hope*. The accusations occasionally had touches of humor. One of these was that we were spreading moral disease in Ceylon by introducing the sinful Western game of "strip poker" to the "Resplendent Land." Not only was this fabrication described in detail by an eyewitness, but then it was stated that strip poker had spread throughout Colombo, corrupting the young of the city. Many young Buddhists were reputed to have been caught playing this horrible game, first introduced into Ceylonese culture by the *Hope*. The ultimate was yet to come: "It has been reported that corpses are brought from the American Ship *Hope* which is in Colombo Harbour, and buried in Colombo Cemetery. It is said that these are corpses of American soldiers who had been wounded in the Vietnam War and were receiving treatment in the *Hope* Hospital Ship."

This was all part of the concentrated effort at harassment faced by Walt Rogers and the *Hope* staff in April of 1968, and he wondered, "This time, could the *Hope* spirit prevail over the vitriol of this minority?" In his heart he knew it would. But how could our dangerous "spies-in-white" make it come about?

# CHAPTER 6

The answer in Colombo was as it has always been with *Hope*. The answer was asserted in the spirit of our nurses and supporting staff. Osler once wrote that "the trained nurse has become one of the great blessings of humanity, taking a place beside the physician and the priest and not inferior to either in her mission." Our success in medicine in our own country has rested upon the development of the team concept in medicine. The lack of this in Ceylon was fertile soil for our beginning.

Our physicians began making friends, establishing that they were no threat to the wary local practitioner. In many instances this was not a real concern, for local physicians such as Dr. John Wilson and Dr. Ivor Obeysekera, highly competent men in their own right, required no reassurance. Both of these physicians could have served on the faculty of any American medical school, and only their love for the people of Ceylon could have kept them in Colombo, functioning in the difficult atmosphere in which they had to practice their skills.

But our girls were the heroines of the first weeks, plotting their course as if the newspapers' allegations fazed them not one whit. Ceylonese students and counterparts came to the ship, were housed, and in a matter of hours the training program was under way. At first the Ceylonese nurses were surprised to find how hard our Hopies worked and that no task was too menial for them. They observed that a clean ward depended upon the nurses' willingness to bend down and clean up something the instant it had been spilled or broken. Under the caste complex of the East, such work was too demeaning for a trained nurse and considered the function of a lower-level worker. Another contrast was that the nurse in Ceylon was virtually ignored by the physician, who felt her observations were unimportant and her ability limited.

The result was not only hospitals lacking cleanliness, organization and patient care but any interest in the patient as a human being as well. Surprise amounting to consternation was seen on the faces of the Ceylonese girls as they observed our physicians on the wards asking our nurses even ordinary questions about the patients' condition. The responsibilities given our nurses in the intensive care unit was beyond their comprehension. Chris Kradjian, our coronary intensive care nurse, was later to be responsible for the opening of Ceylon's first coronary intensive care unit and the training of all of its personnel. But the Ceylonese nurses were literally frightened by the responsibilities our nurses carried in their daily work.

The *Hope* nurse has a way with her that has won her affection, respect and gratitude on three continents. She smiles, teaches and gives care in a manner that is measured with patience, never offensive. She knows that change cannot come overnight, if at all. It's difficult to believe, but there is no greater early accomplishment for all of our girls than to see a local nurse learn that kindness to a patient is frequently as important as the medication. The gratitude of a crying child on a pediatric ward who is patted instead of spanked for crying is one of those small but important victories. Early in the mission, it was unusual to see a local nurse comfort a child, for along with everyone else in the medical system they had grown to believe that this would take too much time. After only a few days of expo-

sure to the *Hope*, there was a dramatic change in attitude. It
was noticed not only by us but by the families of patients. Finally, even the press began to concede that perhaps we could
bring some good to the country if we taught their nurses to be
kinder to patients. A small victory, yes! But it was our first.

Our physicians meanwhile were also proving that it is people
as individuals who are basically important. Each was making a
friend of his Ceylonese counterpart and getting his program
started in his own way. It was difficult for our specialists to remain reticent, for the need for help was all too apparent. They
knew that to be too aggressive would only offend the highly sensitive and proud Ceylonese, but as they walked through the
wards and clinics and saw the massive problems, their impatience grew.

The Colombo General Hospital is a huge complex with thousands of beds. Patients from all over Ceylon come here because
they believe it to be the best medical center in the country. It is
overcrowded, with hundreds of patients on floor care, and in
Colombo General, floor care meant just that. The patient carried
a bamboo straw mat to the hospital with him and slept on the
floor, when there were no beds available. Some beds already
held more than one patient. Our thirty-five volunteer specialists,
many from the finest teaching institutions in the United States,
itched to offer suggestions, but had to wait to be asked. Each
knew he was being judged. A few were impatient.

Many of the answers were so obvious. The inefficiency of the
system of government medicine was one. There were patients in
each ward who had been in the hospital for months awaiting
surgery. But each had a number and must wait his turn. The senior member of the department of radiology refused to do more
than a small number of examinations a day, about 25 per cent of
the normal work load of a radiologist at home, and so everyone
waited. He was too senior to be censored, too protected to be
removed. The surgeons themselves rarely completed their operating schedules, and patient after patient was rescheduled for

another day. Highly trained and well-skilled assistants could not proceed without their preceptor's permission, and this was rarely given. The constant complaint was that there was not enough time. Despite this, at the General everything stopped for ten A.M. tea, and nothing whatsoever moved between one and three in the afternoon. If anyone wanted to stop the world and get off, Colombo General was the place to do it.

This was all part of the challenge to us, and none of it was a surprise. In our own culture time is terribly important. We believe that in every waking hour we must produce. The Ceylonese physician, in his own way, feels that he is making an equal sacrifice. The life of a patient is more impersonal to him, and perhaps he is the wiser for not concerning himself with what illness may do to a patient's family. We were determined that before the year was over the Ceylonese physicians would have the opportunity to be exposed to our concern for their people. We were not going to force it down their throats but instead would let the example and the attitude of our people themselves teach the lesson for us.

We had allies in the local profession, men who wanted more than anything else to see the system changed. Without *Hope* they didn't have a chance. With our help, men like Wilson, Obeysekera and Dr. Hamza may yet be able to smile.

Walt Rogers felt that the way to reach the resisting Ceylonese physician was to repeatedly reassure the people and the press of their professional expertise. We found this was not the solution, for they began to believe our misplaced propaganda, and it gave fodder to the leftists who wrote that if we were no better than their own physicians, the government should send the Yankees home. Walt finally reached the end of his patience when the local resistants and government bureaucrats together attempted to force totally incurable cases on the *Hope*. With such patients, we could neither teach nor win friends. Each death was headlined in the leftist press; when a patient was rejected, he became "too difficult a case for the American doctors." I do believe this was the critical period in which *Hope* might have willingly left this resplendent but confused land.

But then the bright spots began to break through. First they came from the people themselves. We had been in Ceylon only one month when Vesack holiday occurred. This was the time of the full moon in May. Our wards were full but many patients had already been discharged, some with dramatic results, such as one man with a reconstructed jaw; another with a new esophagus—rebuilt after the ravages of cancer. The people were bringing gifts of fruit or cloth, but so submerged were we in our policy troubles we had not recognized the progress made. At the time of the threefold celebration of Buddha—his birth, enlightenment and death—thousands had come into Colombo to look at the display of twenty-six enormous pandals almost fifty feet high, each of which pictured a story or episode in the life of Buddha. Each was surrounded by multicolored bulbs, and loudspeakers blared forth the story of the scene. There were puppet shows and dansala stands where fruit drinks were served free to the pilgrims who had made the trip. The celebrations lasted through the night, but what was most impressive to us—and apparently to the Ceylonese physicians—was that thousands upon thousands also came to the dock to see the great white ship of *Hope*. It was almost as if Buddha had taken a hand.

Then our old friend Harry Hatharasinghe, who loved us and was loved by us all, gave a party at his home for the entire staff as if to show all that *Hope* was truly welcome. The garden was decorated with hanging lanterns, and intertwining palm fronds framed the entrance gate. A picture of the S. S. *Hope* occupied the center of the stage. All of Harry's relatives were there and he had brought in Kandyan dancers, sitar players and a cobra dancer. The classic supper menu included the traditional string hoppers (a vermicelli patty) and egg hoppers (a poached egg on a cupped pancake type of bread), the traditional seerfish and many other delicacies. Harry made everyone feel as if all Ceylon loved them.

The next morning several of our staff physicians walked
through the now overflowing wards on the *Hope* with a different spring to their steps. They felt the warmth and gratitude of
the patients; the greetings of the Ceylonese house officers
seemed more sincere. As they heard the early morning sounds
from pediatrics, they thought of the lame who were already
walking and the blind who were already seeing as a result of
their efforts. They suddenly knew that in a few short weeks they
had bridged a gap, and while much remained to be done, the
first group of doctors had made a good start. As they piled into
the truck to go to Colombo General, they were silent. The massive white buildings that occupied the several square blocks in
downtown Colombo were soon before them. Today it somehow
looked different, better.

One of the staff reflected upon the thoughts of Louis Pasteur,
read many years before. "One does not ask of one who suffers:
What is your country and what is your religion? One merely
says, you suffer, this is enough for me; You belong to me and I
shall help you." He straightened up and wondered, does this
apply only to the sick, or may it apply to the doctor as well? He
went through the doors with a renewed determination and
heightened understanding that now could not result in failure.

# CHAPTER 7

As the monsoon rains began, the Kandy contingent left for that inland city. Trepidation had been overcome by curiosity and excitement; also, a relief to get away from Colombo and its "big people" of Ceylon.

The loading of the two Land Rovers in front of the Taprobane Hotel in downtown Colombo stirred memories of the migrant workers in *The Grapes of Wrath*. There was hardly an empty space; personal belongings were inside, outside and slung across the tops of the white vehicles with the proud letters Project HOPE on their sides.

The team was composed of five nurses and a lab technician, led by Gracie Tucker, a diminutive girl from New Haven, Connecticut, and cheered by the irrepressible Mo Gallagher, Newport's gift to *Hope*. Each time they felt all was ready for departure, Mo had another last-minute suggestion.

"Have we got enough peanut butter?" she asked. "What about soap powder? You know we'll never be able to get any up there; and if *Hope* internal communications are up to par, we may be scraping the dirt off if we run out." Though the latter was said with tongue in cheek, experienced Hopies prefer to leave nothing to chance.

Record players, linen, insect repellent, medicines for personal use—primarily an ample supply of Lomotil to slow the inevitable gastric response to local food—and bottled water for the trip. Hopies never drink the local water or trust the local ice for the first two weeks of any mission. Thereafter they are perfectly willing to concede that all water is boiled and ice sterile, a conclusive demonstration of the power of mind over stomach and its occupying bacteria.

It was Aralen day, that is the day for our malaria prevention pills, so this was not forgotten. Recent malarial outbreaks on the island had all of us concerned, and in the hills the rainy season was an ideal breeding time for the mosquito.

Finally, as the morning sun rose in the eastern sky, everything was ready, and the six girls piled into the lead Rover, one on top of the other. They planned to complete the journey before noon. They had been reluctant to leave without any physicians, fearing a rebuff in Kandy because of the absence of full-fledged doctors. Nurses simply do not get the respect they deserve in this nation, as in so many others, but the girls realized that coping with this attitude was part of their job. The nurse must be properly recognized, and this little band was determined that she should be. We felt that by sending the girls by themselves, with some physicians to follow within a few days, we asserted our own faith in their ability and self-sufficiency.

The Rovers took off with a roar and the smell of scorched rubber on the pavement. In unison, the girls shouted one of the most frequently-to-be-used Sinhalese phrases of the year, "Slow down, slow down!" "*Hemin yanna, hemin yanna!*" Their driver grinned, his white teeth splitting his dark Tamil face with a smile, and, of course, he shook his head negatively from side to side meaning "yes." Then he accelerated further and Mo appealed to her God for protection.

Every ride in Ceylon is a genuine thrill. The drivers seem to have either an unerring instinct for what hides behind the next turn in the road or else a supreme faith in Buddha. Whatever happens, the next life will be better.

The city streets leading to the winding road for Kandy were already thick with people streaming to work. Barefoot children were carrying pans of water from some central fountain to their homes, others were selling fruit or breakfast curries from small trays carried atop their heads. No one seemed hurried, except the drivers. Horns blew indiscriminately; pedestrians rarely paid any attention. If they did not move, the driver simply went around them, frequently grazing them slightly with a fender. Should his detour take him to the wrong side of the street, he simply charged headlong down that side. If oncoming traffic—anything from a small Japanese import to an ancient two-decker London bus—was heading straight for him, both drivers played the Ceylonese version of "chicken." At the last moment one or the other or both would give way, and unerringly each would turn in the proper direction to avert a head-on collision.

Repeated urgings of caution from the passengers only diverted the driver's attention.

Somehow our little band made it through the city and headed on to the narrow, curving road that was to take them on to Kandy. Now they had their first view of the real beauty of Ceylon, as the serpentine road wound first into the foothills and then into the mountains of Ceylon. Everything was green, for there really are no seasons in Ceylon—just dry, wet and wetter.

On either side they began to see the neatly kept rice fields, their canals and terraces giving the appearance of plenty. And everywhere were the wooden carts, pulled by plodding water buffalo, always with a barefoot attendant in front of them. One of the great insults in Ceylon is to call someone a buffalo. The animal is said to be so stupid—even though useful—that he will continue to plod forward off the edge of a cliff unless he is turned aside by his guide.

In the same rice fields in which the buffalo slowly dragged behind him an ancient wooden plow, entire families of cheerful, seemingly contented people tended the paddies. In some, naked children frolicked in the mud or in a slightly clearer water hole nearby. Some washed, some played, others were doing laundry in the only water available to them. These were the delightful, friendly "little people" of Ceylon. They were unspoiled by the veneer of the European-trained bureaucrat or the relatively sophisticated city dweller involved in planning the future but whose real allegiance was still to the past.

The "little people" of Ceylon were caught up in what seems to many an impossible situation. Perhaps because of hopelessness or else a deep religious belief in redemption in the next world or return to this one in another situation, there was a curious contentment, or possibly apathy. They were certainly without money and material things. They inhabited a sheltered, shut-in world. They had enough to eat, even if not all the right things. Those who needed consolation chewed the betel nut, which brought a feeling of well-being, while the dye from its juice stained the teeth and lips a bright red. They smiled about the future, lived in the past, existed in the present. Their hearts were warm.

Each time the drivers had to slow down or stop in a crowded *pettah* or marketplace in a village, the people would crowd around the vehicles in droves. Mo soon discovered that they were just as curious to see the white skin and strange Western clothes she wore as she was about their appearance and their clothes.

"At first I felt like an animal in the zoo," she said, "and as the crowds grew in size I felt a little frightened.

" 'Gracie, what should we do, how should we react?' I said. 'Are they going to steal our stuff? They look so poor. Let's buy some of those curry dishes they're selling. Maybe that will make them feel we're friendly.' "

"If you buy them we'll have to eat them, and you know how they'll burn going down. Well—what do you think, girls?"

The vote was to buy, eat and pray, and keep saying the traditional greeting, "*Abuyovan.*" The driver sat amused. Although he could not understand their rapid conversation, he had driven

Europeans before and knew their reactions. Wise man that he was, he knew this always meant a few rupees for the village and extra curry specialties for himself. The girls inevitably, as did others, turned to him for advice on what to pay, holding up the rupees for him to see they meant business.

"It didn't take us long," said Mo, "to find that after the first few villages we were overpaying and Abdullah Mohammed was just being charitable to the villagers. Besides, he spoke English pretty well, but then we didn't realize that."

"We found, too," she later wrote, "that in these little places with no telephones and few newspapers they already knew about the *Hope*. Unlike the pseudo-sophisticates of Colombo, the 'little people' already had developed a genuine respect for *Hope*. The few who could speak English were proud that the ship had come to Ceylon. They explained that some of the villagers had relatives who had either been on the *Hope* as patients or who had seen our physicians at work in the clinics. They already spoke of the value we would leave behind in the skills being shown to their doctors. These, the *big* 'little people,' had already accepted the *Hope* in their hearts. Only a few short miles outside of Colombo, and the gentle ones—those who needed us the most—had given us the assurance that eventually 'we would overcome.' "

Soon after, the two-car caravan started to climb into the steep hills. Village after village, places with strange, unpronounceable names were passed. Fewer buffaloes and more elephants were seen now. The elephants were hard at work, some carrying logs, others palm fronds for the roofs of the simple houses under construction. Each elephant had a small mahout sitting on his massive back who carried a wicked-looking knife that resembled a broad curved scimitar. At the side of the elephant walked another mahout brandishing a long pole with a pointed tip. He gave the elephant his orders in a quiet voice and with an occasional prod. Mo explained to the others: "The mahout on top has the knife in case the elephant goes berserk. He is supposed to kill him. This doesn't happen often, but a berserk elephant can destroy an entire village and kill loads of people."

"From the size of the mahout, the knife and the neck of that elephant, I really doubt he would do much good," answered Gracie.

Just then another elephant passed on the opposite side of the road, obviously returning from work much too early in the day. "Abdullah, what is that elephant doing?" one of the girls asked the driver. "Getting off early?"

"No, Missy, no elephant goes home early. Look at his back legs, they are tied together only with a small piece of hemp which he could snap in a moment. But he will not. No, elephant is very smart. He has been a bad elephant and must have refused to obey. He is being punished and brought home. The hemp on his legs stops him from taking a full stride, but then he knows he is being punished. Elephant very smart, Missy, oh very smart."

The weather became cooler as they drove farther up into the hills and it was apparent why Ceylon had been called the "Second Eden" by the early Islamic traders. The hillsides were a collage of greens. They were beautifully terraced with rice paddies, carefully constructed with water beds held between logs and furrows of mud. The sky and the trees of the surrounding jungle forest swam in the pools, a quiet reflection.

Now the darker green of the tea plantations began to dominate the highland slopes. Tea is the life blood of Ceylon, its most important export. Each plantation seemed neater, better tended than the one before. Along the roadside, wherever there was neither tea nor rice, foliage of every variety abounded: palms and trees filled with every type of tropical fruit—the mango, breadfruit, jak, pawpaw and the ever-present banana. And one wondered how anyone in Ceylon could ever go hungry.

Higher and higher, into the land where clouds covered the mountaintops and the surprising waterfalls cascaded down their sides. Suddenly as the two cars came around a mountain curve, Abdullah slowed to a stop at the roadside. They looked down into a precipitous gorge of about two thousand feet while across the valley a majestic mountain rose. Abdullah pointed to it and whispered with quiet reverence, "That is Adam's Peak." The peak itself reached high above all the surrounding hills, and the plateau at its top was marked by a sudden depression. Its seven-thousand-foot summit can only be reached by a tortuous four-mile ascending trail.

"What is Adam's Peak?" asked the girls.

With no loss of reverence, Abdullah explained: "Adam's Peak has something for everybody. First, I tell you the Buddhists believe that the holy footprint of Buddha is there. The Hindus believe it is the mountain of their god Siva. The Moslems believe that when Adam was thrown out of paradise, he stood there doing penance for a thousand years. At the end of his penance, he was reunited with Eve and lived in Ceylon for centuries creating the human race.

"No matter what you believe, it is a holy place and pilgrims visit it constantly. Even you Christians would feel the holy spirits if you climbed it. The peak gives consolation to all who live in these hills, for it can be seen from every part of this land. It would be the same if you could see Calvary every morning that you awakened in your Christian world."

The remainder of the trip to Kandy was a relatively silent one, each traveler lost in her own reflections. Adam's Peak had deeply impressed these Western girls. They passed Kitagulla, the last large village before their arrival in Kandy. Silence gave way once more to anticipation and excitement as the caravan came around a final bend in the road and into the city of Kandy.

They drove through the crowded streets and around the beautiful two-mile Kandy Lake in the center of this crystal mountain city, past the revered Temple of the Tooth, across the bridge over the lake till they came to the Hotel Suisse, their home for the next five months.

The Suisse was an old British hotel, sitting high on a hill overlooking the lake. The girls were somewhat awed as the Rovers climbed the hill to the entrance. The building looked imposing, regal—and they feared they would not have the right clothes, not knowing that in this massive building they were to be almost the only guests.

Abdullah pulled the car into the parking yard at the side of the lobby. Now the girls were better able to see that the beautiful old building was in some disrepair. Paint was needed everywhere, and only a few window-type air conditioners were visible. The lobby, large and modestly furnished, with tile floors and high ceilings, was open on one side. Batiks hung on the walls, showing traditional scenes of the Perahera celebration (a religious parade) which is held annually in Kandy.

Their spirits were instantly lifted by the appearance of a squadron of smiling, barefoot, long-gowned, white-coated gentlemen, the staff of the Hotel Suisse, gathered to welcome and help them. They were led by a straight-backed, handsome, white-haired headman with a magnificent moustache curled upward onto both cheeks. This was John, sixty years old, a proud and proper servant who we were later to discover had served Lord Louis Mountbatten during the Second World War.

It was apparent he had learned the art of command, for it required only a glance from him to send the other servants scurrying in every direction. His delight at the arrival of the *Hope* contingent was obvious, and he became a fast and true friend. As the nurses were signing in he had readied a welcome pot of tea, served in a reading room just off the lobby. This room, which led out into a small garden overlooking the lake, would become a daily meeting place and "happy-hour" site.

Mo and Grace went to their rooms on the second floor in the east wing. The rooms were sparsely furnished with old metal beds, tired mattresses and ceiling fans spinning lazily overhead. The floors were dark brown, waxed wood. The bathroom had an aged tub, a shower of unknown vintage and a drainage channel for both along the stone floor. But the Suisse had a charm all its own. This was home, and the girls were determined to enjoy it.

Mo said, "Now look, the credo of the *Hope* is 'be flexible,' right? So let's be flexible and turn on the faucets and see if water really comes out, maybe even hot. And don't . . . *do not* touch those water bottles and thermoses on the table, not for a few days anyhow. Then we can stop fooling ourselves and get used to the local bugs. The *Hope* manual says spray under the beds every night and inhale the sweet odor of DDT instead of the fresh air. Take your pick—an occasional cockroach, a few mosquitoes, or air pollution."

Grace suggested they get settled and meet down in the room by the garden where they could plan their day. Dr. Bibile, the dean of the school, and Dr. Sangakkara, the superintendent of the hospital, were due that afternoon. "They'll want to meet us all, so get into your uniforms and let's look like nurses, not tourists. And please—no cameras for the time being."

A few moments later Grace looked at the group around her and wondered, probably not for the first time, "How well would they really do?" Her nurses must seem a tiny contribution to the Kandy Hospital complex, which was then housing over a thousand patients. How could they make any real impression? Yet Grace had been here before with the survey team and knew the task well; that is why she had been chosen as the chief nurse of the unit. A scant five feet tall, with large round eyes and a dimpled chin, Grace might appear an odd choice to convince the proud Dr. Sangakkara that improvements had to be made but we who knew of her service in Africa were certain that the doctor had more than met his match.

Then there was beautiful Inge Hansen, a laboratory technician from Copenhagen who had been with *Hope* for three years. She would need all of her Scandinavian persistence and strength to climb each morning some twelve hundred feet to the highest part of the hospital to reach the laboratory. There she was assigned to work with a pathologist who had little faith in technicians and who did not believe in allowing emergencies to break the peace of Poya day or after sundown hours.

Mo Gallagher sat opposite Grace trying to imagine what she was to face in the pediatric ward the next day.

Barbara Kushwara and Mel Foltz, both veterans of past missions, were also present. They were both slender and small, and capable. Grace felt they would be just fine. She reflected that the four of them were so slight in appearance that Dean Bibile might think the *Hope* was indeed a corps of Lilliputians. The last member of the team was Ann Farley, a newcomer. Was it wise, she thought, to have sent one of the new girls out? Even in the protective environment of the ship the cultural shock syndrome is severe and here Ann would be put immediately on her own.

They had time for only a few moments of discussion when John came into the room. He bowed and announced they had guests. Dr. Bibile and Dr. Sangakkara had arrived. The girls stood as the men entered the room. The Kandy Kids were about to face their first challenge.

# CHAPTER 8

Dr. Bibile was a self-assured, handsome man in his late forties. A warm smile and accompanying words of welcome put the girls at ease. Dr. Sangakkara was older and heavier with the back and shoulders of an athlete. The hair that was missing from the top of his head was growing from his ears, in Ceylon an admired distinction and sign of virility. From that moment on, to Mo and all of the Hopies he was to be old "Hairy Ears." Though he did not seem delighted at the prospect of *Hope*'s appearance in Kandy, he was later to become one of our best friends.

The amenities concluded, Bibile asked, "Shall we go over to the hospital and see where you can best begin?"

"By all means, Doctor, that is what we are here for," Grace answered.

Within five minutes the group was at the Kandy Hospital. The square in front of the hospital was clogged with people, some staff but mostly patients en route to the clinics, or families of patients on their way to visit the sick. As they looked up the side of the hill to where ward on top of ward had been constructed, they realized what Grace had meant when she said she hoped their legs were as strong as their spirits. The buildings,

like the paddies, were terraced upward toward the top of the
hill to a height that made Inga feel she would need seven-
league boots to reach the lab at the top. Would anyone ever
climb up to the lab to dispute a result? More than likely they
would avoid it as much as possible. This could only complicate
a training mission, one which she already feared because she
had been told of the edgy attitude of the pathologist.

The first shock was the pediatric ward, Mo Gallagher's baili-
wick. It was large, but not large enough to give each child his
own bed. And it was dark, dusty and dreary. The youngsters
seemed all the sicker for it. Children with infectious disease
shared cribs with those not so ill. One small boy, critically ill
with hepatitis, bedded with one convalescing from pneumonia
—not a wise exposure for either of them. There was no area
where convalescent children could play or even walk about, and
nothing is more difficult than to keep an almost well child in
bed.

Nor had a place been set aside where healthier children could
eat; their meals were served in the beds in which they lay with
other, sicker children. It was little wonder that cross infection
and relapse were common. Parasites were inevitably traded between patients on the same linen or on the same soiled mattress
when there was no linen, which was often the case.

Mo could hardly restrain herself. She had seen these conditions before and knew what should and could be done. The administrator explained that certainly they knew the crowding was
wrong but they were poor and so busy at the hospital that it
could not be helped. Mo knew better. She had seen many of the
nurses and aides standing about doing nothing because of the
lack of supervision and organization.

"Quiet, Irish," she said to herself. "Remember we all promised
to suggest, not order; we are going to be sweet and patient." But
how furious it made her inside to know what a scrub brush and
clean water could do. "One lousy can of paint," she thought,
"would make everyone on this ward feel better." She made up

her mind then and there to make her first goal: a can of paint, some brushes, soap, water and extra buckets. That wasn't what she learned at nursing school, but she knew that no child could ever truly get well in that dark and dingy ward.

To her it seemed strange that in the economically poor countries where she had been, the philosophy had always been not to make the most of what facilities the people had. Instead, they demanded a new hospital or a new building, and if the money were not forthcoming from the government for these, there was an immediate retreat into self-pity. Don't take care of what you have, commiserate and in a way destroy the meager resources with which you have been provided. Rarely do those who plead for more realize that in their neglect of what they have, they destroy tomorrow. Mo was determined that lesson number one was going to be "Make the best of what the Lord has given you." How could they look at these children and not feel that something better could be done? Give the coming generation a chance for something better!

The experiences of the other girls were similar. Each was given a choice of a ward, one they felt they could in some way improve, both by example and teaching.

A good example of the kind of problem faced was to be found on the adult wards in medicine and surgery, where a minor diplomatic crisis was precipitated when the *Hope* nurses performed a normal and mundane nursing task. The Kandyan nurses did not empty bedpans nor aid the patients in similar situations, considering such chores beneath them. Therefore, not only did many seriously ill patients suffer from both discomfort and filth, but more frequently than not accidents occurred which resulted in unsanitary wards. When our *Hope* nurses instinctively helped patients in the most delicate circumstances rather than wait for the ever-absent orderlies or aides, the patients wondered why their own nurses did not do the same thing. The Ceylonese nurses reacted defensively, and it fell upon Grace Tucker to persuade and educate them tactfully. No part of patient care, she

explained, was beneath the dignity of a good nurse. Elementary
as this may sound, it was the first crack in the caste system of
patient care.

By the end of the first week, the Kandy Kids were beginning
to feel sufficient confidence to move forward. The arrival of two
of our volunteer physicians from the ship gave momentum to
their efforts. Dr. Jo Ann Cornet, a pediatrician from Chicago,
was particularly effective. The chief of pediatrics at Kandy, Dr.
Herb Aponso, had been aware of the faults that Mo had found
in the wards but had not fought to bring about change. With the
added strength of the specialist from Chicago and the enthusiastic energy of little Mo, the changes came.

Mops and scrub brushes came out first. Mo organized all of
the nurses in the ward into a clean-sweep effort which resulted in
the cleaning out of two rooms in the pediatric complex. All of
the children with infectious diseases were placed in one area—
not a perfect solution by any means, but at least those children
still free of infectious disease were protected from those who
were contagious.

A playroom was organized for the convalescents who were
ambulatory, and toys appeared from the *Hope* in Colombo.
During mealtime, the playroom was converted to a child's din-
ing room in which each child who was able carried a small
chair to a low common table where all ate together. The children enjoyed it as a game and ate the not-too-appetizing rice
and curry diet with renewed gusto. Convalescence was short-
ened, nurses devoted more time to essential tasks, and morale
throughout the whole pediatric service was vastly improved.
The students and the doctors were more spirited on their
rounds, and Dr. Aponso became a devotee of bedside teaching.

Mo then took the next step. She suggested that the local
nurses divide the wards into management areas, each to be su-
pervised by a nursing team. Thus a very sick child could be
completely cared for by one particular nurse, while others not in
need of intensive care could benefit from the team approach.

Nurses began to communicate between teams and shifts, and as their enthusiasm increased so too did their efficiency. The importance of fondling a sad child, or tying a pretty ribbon in a little girl's hair was demonstrated. How simple, how important! The ward was becoming humanized, producing a whole new attitude in physician, patient, nurse and student. Small victories? Perhaps. But how big they were to little Mo, for she knew what they meant to Ceylon. The concept of team medicine was being introduced.

When she returned exhausted each night to the Hotel Suisse to be greeted by a smiling, erect headman with fresh tea on his tray, she could relax with the knowledge of a job well started. At the end of every day the *Hope* nurses and physicians would gather at that room by the garden for "happy hour" and to exchange experiences of the day. Each had a victory and some days each had a defeat. But collectively they knew they had been accepted in Kandy.

Dean Bibile had become "Bibs" to all of them. He frequently invited the entire group to his home for an excellent curry and an evening of music appreciation. Bibs had tapes of every variety of music from traditional Ceylonese, classical, opera to contemporary. He could provide hours of listening, and it was on evenings such as these that he and our unit members really learned to know one another. They discussed everything from medicine to politics. They traded dreams and aspirations, thoughts on war, peace, the future. Most of all they learned a mutual respect and trust. Soon, to all those still aboard the S. S. *Hope* anchored in the waters off Colombo, Kandy became *the* envied assignment.

It wasn't all work at Kandy. The people of the entire city had taken to the *Hope* crew. Invitation followed invitation, and an intimacy and understanding developed. On Pre-Poya afternoons there were picnics at the Botanical Gardens with only a break for cover to escape a sudden drenching monsoon shower. In these gardens were the trees and flowers of all of Asia, and the local citizens were very proud of them. On other days there were treks into the countryside to look at batiks made by experts. The girls would rummage through dozens of patterns, haggling over prices and enjoying the game of bargaining as much as the seller. But when the price was reached, the seller always had the better of the deal and would bow his head, bringing his hands together in traditional fashion and say joyously *"Bohoma stuthi,"* the Sinhalese phrase for "thank you." On occasion they were fortunate enough to watch the batiks they had ordered actually being made.

Another favorite trip on the Poya day weekend was to motor to the beach at Trincomalee, one hundred and thirty miles or more away. This stretch of beach could only be reached after traversing the arid jungle of mid-central Ceylon where one drove for miles, never seeing a settlement or human being. Gorgeous birds, frolicking monkeys and wild elephants were inhabitants here. The elephant roamed at night, but eluded the cameras of some of the more daring *Hope* staffers who tried to take their pictures. On one occasion an elephant almost succeeded in getting one of our finer volunteer surgeons. Fortunately the surgeon had the wisdom, as he heard the elephant crashing through the dry brush, to run as fast as he could for his car. The local drivers, who considered anyone who attempted this type of photography to be totally insane, always kept the motor running. The physician threw himself headlong through the open rear door sans picture, sans camera, and utterly terrified as the car roared off down the narrow road. The only sound that could be heard over the noise of the engine was the trumpeting of the elephant, victorious in the protection of his privacy.

Trincomalee, however, was a wonderful haven. Its beaches had picturesque names such as the Blue Lagoon or Cove Beach. The water was crystal clear and even within twenty yards of the shore one could look down and find a breathtaking variety of tropical fish. Mo, Grace, Barbara, and Mel all became veteran "snorkelers" after only a few short weeks.

An inexhaustible supply of large lobsters inhabited the ocean bottom, close to the rocks about a mile from shore. When the palate demanded it, Hopies could rent a small boat, spear guns, and catch dinner in an afternoon. They usually sought help for these expeditions by extending invitations for the weekend to the doctors or the students on the ship in Colombo.

Fresh catch in hand, they would then find their favorite guesthouse (these are government-run tourist houses) where the lobster could be prepared and the balance of the meal purchased for almost nothing. Coca-Cola, beer, a guitar, and the trials of both the week behind and the week ahead were momentarily forgotten.

It was at the conclusion of one of these weekends, as they were driving back toward Kandy, that Mo, now brimming with contentment and reflection, thought of her children waiting for her in the pediatric ward. When she returned to the hotel, she wrote a poem that concluded:

> I am a receiver who came to give
> I have had my eyes opened wide
> I realize how fortunate I am
> Please, never-never let them be half-closed again.

# CHAPTER 9

It was mid-June in Colombo. The hospital wards were full, the nurses' training program and other phases of the paramedical teaching were moving forward slowly but surely. But progress was much too slow on the professional level at Colombo General and the medical school. The executive committee of our *Hope* staff met frequently, attempting to find the reason why.

Walt Rogers was unable to put his finger on anything specific, for the local physicians had been friendly and courteous socially. But professionally, with the exception of the pediatric and internal medicine services, they were reluctant to participate in a joint teaching program. The seniority system so traditional to European training persisted at its worst in Ceylon.

We were in no position to bring pressure upon the incompetents, and yet their very insecurity because of their awareness of their deficiencies was denying education to the students of modern Ceylon. These students were bright, eager and open-minded. They were not permitted to ask questions or offer opinions; those who did on occasion were humiliated by their teachers in front of their fellow students.

One day, a *Hope* volunteer returned to the ship with a story we found hard to believe. He had been on ward rounds with a local professor, some house officers and a group of students. On many services student participation had only begun after the arrival of the *Hope*. He reported:

"The professor seemed intent on keeping the students quiet and asked them little. The few questions he directed their way were difficult and in some instances not even germane. The students answered only with reluctance and never disagreed."

"Good heavens," piped up one of our own professors who was listening to the story, "if my students didn't disagree with me or at least question some of the things I said, I would feel they were losing interest."

"Wait, it gets worse. Finally one of the students did venture an opinion on a case, and unfortunately it was incorrect. The professor beamed in triumph, and instead of using the opportunity to illustrate the vital points of diagnosis, he pointed to the floor beneath the patient's bed and shouted, 'Under there, under there on your hands and knees and don't come out until I call you.'

"The young man flushed furiously but humbly crawled under the bed amidst the guffaws of the rest of the students and the sarcastic comments of the house officers, each of whom vied for the approval of the professor.

"I was shocked," he went on. "I didn't know what to say or do. I didn't laugh, I felt more like crying. Not for the victim on the floor, for he would respect seniority no matter what the price. But what could the future of medical education in Ceylon be with this type of behavior? Medicine is a humble science, an art of understanding and loving people. The professor succeeded in humiliating me, not the student. I simply couldn't continue the rounds and mumbled an excuse that I had to return to the ship for a conference, and left."

"Well, that's what we're up against," said one of the listeners. "Sometimes I think that Kipling was right, never the twain shall meet."

"But it must," said still another, "for if it doesn't this country will most assuredly go down the drain. Medicine is only a part of it, but it's as good a place to begin as anywhere else. Let's make it a promise among ourselves that we will constantly remind the teachers and staff at the hospital of the words of William Osler." A copy of Osler's remarks on how a hospital stays a good hospital was found and his words cited:

"The work of an institution in which there is no teaching is rarely first class. There is not that keen interest, nor the thorough study of the cases, nor amid the exigencies of the busy life is the hospital physician able to escape clinical slovenliness unless he teaches and *in turn is taught by assistants and students.* It is, I think, safe to say that in a hospital with students in the wards the patients are more carefully looked after, their diseases are more fully studied and few mistakes made."

"It's too bad that we can't frame that and hang it on every wall in the hospital and in the Minister's office too," replied Walt. The meeting broke up on the same note as many others had—a quiet determination to move ahead to a breakthrough.

The spirit of some of our staff was exceeded only by their patience. Barry Panter was being well received by the pediatricians and was blessed with personable and capable volunteer specialists to help him. Bob Kradjian, our coordinator of surgery, had a more difficult task. He had the medical prima donnas of Colombo to deal with. The surgeons were competent and experienced and treasured their seniority above all else. The chief of the service frequently stated that he stopped counting the number of major operations he had performed after he passed the twenty-five thousand mark. Even allowing for slight exaggeration, I doubt that anyone at home could match his record. The difficulty was that some of his techniques had not changed in twenty years, despite medical advances. Some were no longer even considered correct. Bob tried in every fashion he knew to encourage the man to realize that to learn or listen to someone else was not demeaning. Surgeons frequently suggest changes in techniques to one another, but not in Ceylon.

More seriously, the operating room procedures followed by his nurses and anesthetists were in sad need of improvement. A

surgeon of his skill deserved better assistance, but at this point
in our stay even suggestions in this area were not welcomed. He
was friendly to Bob, frequently invited him to his home, but still
did not let down his guard on professional matters. Bob knew
that he had gained the man's respect, for he himself was a
highly competent surgeon. How he stood the frustration I will
never know. No doubt having his good wife Chris, one of our
top-drawer *Hope* nurses, at his side was a constant source of
strength.

When Barry was unable to bring about much improvement at
the hospital ashore, he tried to persuade his counterpart in pediatrics to come to the ship. He achieved a partial victory in obtaining the assignment of house officers (these are the equivalent
of our hospital residents) and determined to make his impact
upon them. He knew that in time and after sufficient exposure
they would accept his teaching and the teaching of others who
joined our staff from the United States every two months.

This became the "battle plan" of the *Hope*. Get the house officers and the students. Deal with the future by working with
those who are the future. Make them realize, however subtly,
that when a man is too proud to learn, professional rigor mortis
is beginning to set in. Make them confident, make them challenge the system from within. Encourage them in the necessity
of participating in their own training at every level, from student to house officer. Be certain that they understand that we
are pointing out the need for renewal within the system, rather
than revolution. Through the medium of the young, we were determined to reach the old.

We were amused at first to find that the Ceylonese surgeons
were referring to our physicians for consultation only those
whom they felt were incurable. Temporarily, we fell into an apparent trap, for we rejected these and asked for routine cases
more suited to our program in which we simultaneously train
nurse, technician, anesthesiologist, resident, student, and endeavor to demonstrate new techniques for even routine proce-

dures to our counterparts. For example, the best method to teach total sterile technique is to demonstrate it, not talk about it. At Colombo General all the evils of a bureaucratically run medical system prevented this. The surgeon's primary responsibility was the operative procedure itself. The supporting anesthesia service was someone else's responsibility. Nor was the technique of the nurses his concern, but rather the concern of the senior nurse. The sterilization and preparation of his supplies and equipment was the province of yet another authority. The inadequacy of the operating room gowns which made it almost impossible to operate without infection was the fault of still another branch of the hospital or the ministry. The finest surgeon in the world could not perform well in such an atmosphere. All suffered from the system, especially the patient.

There was a high number of postoperative deaths. Also patients in need of immediate care had to wait months for admission, while others demanded and got hospitalization even though surgery could not be scheduled for months. A pregnant woman could ask for hospitalization while early in her pregnancy and be cared for until delivery time. It was not within the province of the physician himself to deny admission. Is it any wonder that he became blasé about patient care unless the case proved especially challenging?

We knew that we had no right or privilege to come in and simply demand change. We were invited guests in a friend's house, yearning to help that friend. We were as powerless as the physicians of Ceylon themselves to force change. But we had to find a way to convince them that because the government had shared their invitation, perhaps we could be a catalyst for change. We could only perform that function if they saw us as an addition to their strength rather than a threat to their prestige.

But the poor are always so proud, and relatively Ceylon is a poor nation. Somehow, the physicians felt that we should have been far superior to them as technicians, while we had no desire to claim such status. We tried to impress them that we are a practical people, that the money they could save by improving their techniques would make possible the purchase of materials sorely needed. They felt that anything they saved would be diverted elsewhere by the government, a point over which we were in no position to argue.

Until the situation gradually remedied itself with the development of mutual trust and confidence, we decided to take the calculated risk of accepting more difficult patients. We knew that each death would be seized upon by a hostile press, talked about by the insecure physician. In its way, this was to be our trial by fire. Each success on the other hand, each evidence of compassion, was to be a lesson to our trainees, be they doctors, students, nurses, or technicians.

This was why J. Karunaratne, a fifteen-year-old, was referred to the ship from the clinics. He was suffering from elephantiasis, a tropical illness in which the lymph channels of one of his lower extremities had been completely obstructed. He had sought medical help, been seen intermittently, but no one accepted the surgical challenge. There were hundreds like him in Ceylon, scant comfort to the afflicted.

Two years before, Karunaratne had noticed the swelling of his leg, fever, chills and redness. The attacks were repeated, and after they finally ceased his leg remained swollen and eventually became grotesque. He had great difficulty even moving around. Children are cruel in their ignorance and his classmates laughed at him and teased him. He continued at school but became psychologically disturbed. He had been helping his father in his small shop, but his appearance made him so self-conscious that he finally discontinued after-school work. Then, he had fallen and fractured his hip on the same side. The break was treated with herbs by an Ayurvedic physician with no improvement and would itself have to be repaired.

He was admitted to the *Hope* and for the first time in two years was treated with kindness by someone other than his own family. Shy, self-conscious and mistrusting at first, he soon learned that our nurses and doctors were really going to help him. His trust and affection then became almost pathetic. The surgeon in charge of his case knew that he must not fail, for to betray this boy's hope would be to destroy his will to live.

Surgery was performed. The swollen tissue on his lower right leg was removed in one piece and all of the lymphatic tissue was trimmed away, leaving a thin layer of stretched skin. This skin was used as a graft and sutured to the remaining muscle, and his hip was repaired. He now has a leg which is the same size as the other, and after weeks of daily physical therapy he learned to walk all over again. The leg is not perfect, but to young Karunaratne and his parents it seemed as if a miracle had been performed.

Still another difficult case was a child of three, Jainathul Umma, who had been severely burned at the age of three months and had never been able to walk. Her legs had been badly scarred and she experienced severe skin and tendon contracture. She had had no medical help, and it is certain that her parents had little thought that anything could be done on the *Hope*. She was admitted and lay in her crib, uncomplaining but unsmiling and dejected. She, too, was operated upon and after a few weeks of physical therapy she was ready for braces and crutches.

The day finally came, and the whole staff watched as the therapist helped Jainathul take her first few steps. Nothing can describe the thrill of the look on a child's face at such a moment. Later, she walked alone. Soon there was competition on the staff to see who could take her outside on the sunny deck of the *Hope* for her daily exercise and walking lesson. She began to smile and laugh, and with her laughter a whole hospital laughed.

Jainathul Umma will never run, nor will she ever be without braces. But at the age of three, she had taught many what the *Hope* stood for and what we were trying so honestly to do.

# CHAPTER 10

Late one evening, following hours of review of progress reports and a long day ashore, I leaned back sipping a drink and reflecting on what I had learned. What kept our volunteer physicians going, and what made them travel halfway around the world to teach and to heal? I had been especially touched by what they had accomplished at the leprosarium, where six hundred patients were set away from the rest of Ceylon and the world outside. These patients had seen the compassion, the willingness to try to help them, when pitifully few others thought they were worth the time.

It had begun when Dave Furnas, a plastic surgeon from the University of Iowa, met a young Ceylonese surgeon, Jeeva Siriwardene, at a party in Colombo. As always when two physicians meet, the polite exchange of pleasantries is followed by queries on special interests. Siriwardene explained, "I have just been appointed the general surgeon at the leprosarium, and it is a thankless task. It has a low priority in our government planning, and I am supposed to concern myself just with emergencies and not too many of those."

"How can that be?" asked Dave. "Isn't there a great deal of reconstructive surgery necessary because of the nature of the disease?"

"Oh, yes," he sighed, "but I have not been trained to do it. It is difficult for me even to get an anesthesiologist to come to the hospital for an emergency, much less for lengthy operations. It's such a pity to watch the numb fingers just rot, and to see the muscles of the arms and legs shrivel away. Our government feels they should be given medicine and sent home in three months' time so that room can be made for someone else. They are each given fifty rupees a month, that's about four dollars in your money. Soon they are unable to work at all, and they simply die. Perhaps it is God's will."

"That's ridiculous; God never willed for man to suffer like that."

"Wait," he smiled, "here in the East we like to believe sometimes that those we either cannot or will not help are being made to suffer for their sins."

"Poppycock! Double poppycock!" This was Margaret Storkan, a dermatologist from California, speaking up. She had wandered across the room and until now had been only an interested listener. "I have been out to that leprosarium, and there are hundreds of patients that can be treated. If you would only clean it up and get some light in there you would see what I mean."

Six-foot-four Dave looked down at her. "Now, Margaret, we've been here long enough to know that you don't come out and say things like that. Here in the East it isn't yes and no, black and white. Instead you temporize and suggest."

Siriwardene was grinning. "Please, Dave, she is right. You see I *was* temporizing. I know of your skill as a plastic surgeon and of your special interest in the reconstructive surgery of the hand. I need noses and faces rebuilt, I need hands made functional, I need feet sufficiently repaired so that these poor people can walk. But I was using the Ceylonese way. I wanted you to ask me if you could come to my hospital. Now Margaret has unmasked my strategy for what it was. Please—will you come?"

Before he could reply, Margaret spoke up.

"Will he come? You bet he'll come, and I'll come with him. They always tease me about being a dermatologist, but I'll show you what a dermatologist can do at the leprosarium, tomorrow if possible."

"It is agreed then. I will see you in the morning." His mission accomplished, he quietly slipped away and joined the other guests.

The next afternoon Margaret and Dave headed for the town of Hendola, the site of the leprosarium, some seven miles outside of Colombo. Their trip took them through the wholesale fish district of the Pettah in the heart of the city. The smell was sickening and the sight almost as bad. Fresh fish and dried fish both lay out on open, unrefrigerated carts. Swarms of flies covered the fish, and as a potential customer approached a stall a brush of the hand would send thousands of the winged insects momentarily on their way, only to return to their target in a moment. Small children rushed around the center of the market carrying large seerfish or baskets of prawns, hawking them to the shoppers or bringing them to the windows of the cars moving slowly down the street. The fish in Ceylon is delicious, if you can forget how it is marketed.

Once away from the market progress was swift across small bridges which spanned several small streams outside Colombo, and soon they were at Hendola. The leprosarium was hardly impressive. There were several large, one-story buildings with open, unscreened windows. Beds were lined in rows along the walls on either side of the room. The linen was dingy and rust-colored as a result of the antiquated water pipes. There was no place for the storage of personal effects, but few patients had anything to store.

The patients themselves were segregated in the various buildings according to their religion rather than the stage of their disease. The Hindus, Buddhists, Christians, and Moslems were each housed with their own. The appearance of the patients was in itself a lesson in the disease. Faces were so distorted by le-

sions that noses and mouths were almost unrecognizable. Some
of the hands were bandaged with wet, dirty-looking bandages
because of the active stage of the illness. Others just sat, their
fingers or toes missing, hands contracted in the classical fashion
of the leper. The hopelessness in the eyes was the most depressing of all. These were the eyes of the condemned, the feared, the
detested. Yes, the forgotten, who were so hard to forget.

Dave and Margaret agreed that whatever had been attempted
on the lepers behalf certainly wasn't visible. The floors and walls
were dirty and badly in need of paint. Flies and mosquitoes
were drawn to the dirty bandages in swarms and the odor, despite the open windows, was overpowering. There was no evidence of any occupational therapy, although reportedly there
were small fruit and vegetable plots outside which were tended
by the patients. A river flowed through the grounds, and this
was where the patients washed or did whatever personal laundry they may have found necessary. It was not a pretty picture.

It was not Siriwardene's fault. Like so many others in Ceylon,
he had probably never visited the place until he was assigned
there.

Margaret turned to Dave and said: "Well, I don't know what
you're going to do, but I saw patients in there with usable
hands. With the director's permission, we're going to clean up
this place and paint it. These poor souls will never in this world
get well in this atmosphere. They couldn't even want to!"

The director seemed surprised but smiled tolerantly.

"They won't help themselves; they have no hope."

"Never mind, I'll get volunteers from the *Hope* and paint and
paint brushes for the lepers who are able to help, and I'll show
you what can be done with this place."

Siriwardene shrugged; "The persistence of a woman. It might
just work. At least it's worth a try."

Margaret excused herself, took the car and driver and headed
back for the ship, determined to get her working party for the
next Poya day. Dave and the director continued on. As they

continued talking Dave learned that Jeeva had taken his residency training in general surgery in Great Britain and had sufficient background to learn the techniques that Dave could demonstrate. Their excitement mounted, and they went from ward to ward selecting the cases they would do together. If this service could be started, it could be carried on throughout the year by both the plastic and orthopedic surgeons. It was too good an opportunity to miss. And what a way to use the gifted hands God had given him. His hands could make the hands of those cripples usable again. He could give life back to men and women who had felt their only fate was to gradually waste away into the pile of dust from which they had come.

The first victory went to the redoubtable dermatologist from Redondo Beach, California. Forty-eight hours after the first visit, this white-haired commander-in-chief, accompanied by the ship's chaplain, led an army of twenty-five volunteers into the town of Hendola. The painters and cleaners were the doctors and nurses of the *Hope* dressed in every conceivable fatigue throwaway outfit that could be found on board. Some of our nation's greatest specialists in dungarees and shirts borrowed from the crew or salvaged from the hold, nurses, ordinarily seen in sparkling white uniforms with never a hair out of place, were in pants, slacks and borrowed shirts, their hair swathed in everything from shower caps to colorful bandanas, their weapons mops, buckets and paint brushes. A motley but determined army.

As soon as they arrived some set to work scrubbing, others mixed the white paint provided by the ship. At first the patients, either from disbelief or shyness, seemed reluctant to join in. Gradually one by one those who were still able to hold a brush came forward and asked if they could help. Within a two-hour period, this army had finished two wards and run out of paint. It was remarkable to see the difference, the brightness, the good cheer. The army had brought its own supply of soft drinks along and shared them with the patients. The patients, not to be outdone, went outside and brought in coconuts which they insisted on sharing. Something happened that afternoon in Hendola— the lepers were no longer unclean and, in the eyes of many, the *Hope* began to look a little better too.

The patients had heard of the singing of their own National Anthem at our arrival, and now they requested an encore, this time for the lepers of Hendola. It was quite a sight. Our staff, a besmeared crew, stood at attention and sang "Sri Lanka"; and then suddenly the lepers, not all of them able to stand but at least sitting upright in their beds, joined in. There were few dry eyes in Hendola that afternoon, but lots of hope.

As our trucks were loaded and ready to depart, one of the patients said to Dr. Storkan: "Americans are nice people. But are they always this way?" Margaret looked at him through her already reddened eyes and said, "We try."

After that episode Dave felt that anything he accomplished might seem anticlimactic, but Jeeva and the patients knew better. The first case to be scheduled involved tendon surgery on a leper's hand. All was in readiness and the surgeons scrubbed. The patient was wheeled into the operating room. The anesthesiologist prepared to give the anesthesia. "Oh, no! No!" Half of the necessary equipment was nowhere to be found. Then the nurse announced that the hospital had also run out of anesthetic. The surgery had to be canceled.

The case was rescheduled for the next day, together with the reconstruction of a collapsed nose, a common problem in leprosy. This time everything went well, despite a paucity of surgical instruments. And so more cases were scheduled for the next week.

When Dave arrived for his next operating day, he discovered all new surgical instruments in the operating theater. Dr. Karagarutum, the hospital superintendent, had spent his total budget allocation for the year in order to provide them. This was the effect of one man's skill and another physician's desire to help the unfortunate. It was the lesson of humility and desire to learn that had been demonstrated by Jeeva Siriwardene. Before the year came to an end, almost every reconstructive procedure possible was to be performed at the leprosarium, and the legacy of learning left behind in the mind and the hands of a young and compassionate Ceylonese surgeon.

Each of the three, Dave, Margaret, and Jeeva, had been living examples of the oath of Hippocrates which they had sworn to follow. The simple promise—"With purity and with holiness I will pass my life and practice my art." This is all they had done, but oh, the hope they had provided!

# CHAPTER 11

Tom and Judy Bowles stood in silence, transfixed by the beauty around them. They were just outside their living-room doors, on a grass patio that extended some thirty feet, then dropped precipitously. It was dusk and the lights of Kandy were beginning to blink on, like fireflies. The Temple of the Tooth was already bathed in brilliance. The lake below glistened under a twilight sky and about them lay the quiet jungle beyond.

The two, with their two little girls, had arrived from New York only a week before. The contrast between the concrete megalopolis and the green tranquillity here was almost incredible, and they could not help marvel that they were here at all, ten thousand miles from home and friends. Tom was a successful thoracic surgeon with a future. Skilled, personable and handsome, he was loved by patients and admired by his colleagues. He had given it all up to become a part of Project HOPE.

A year earlier he had served a short tour with the ship in Colombia. The experience had altered his entire perspective. He deeply loved to teach, felt compassion for people and demonstrated an intense desire to help the hopeless. He had searched for a comparable way to serve at home but found none. He offered then to join our Foundation staff and was now the director of our program in Kandy.

Tom, Judy and family had arrived two months after the Kandy Kids and were welcomed with open arms. The caste system and social structure of Ceylon being what they are, a male leader was in definite demand. One of our physician volunteers from the ship, Bill McCafferty, had filled in nobly, but a permanent "leader" was an obvious necessity.

The Bowleses had been brought up to date quickly by Gracie Tucker, and after that Tom had thrown himself into his task with enthusiasm. Within only a few days he had developed a deep friendship with Bibs and was making headway with Dr. Sangakkara. The latter was somewhat more difficult, or so it seemed on the surface. He was gruff and grumpy, at times disagreeable. All felt this was a cover-up for a warmhearted man, but until now none had found his point of entry.

Tom was thirty-seven, slender and almost boyish in appearance —L'il Abner with brains. Outgoing and enthusiastic, he knew that Dr. Sangakkara's friendship was not only essential but that a friend was surely hiding beneath that bald head and massive shoulders. Noticing that he had the physique of an old athlete, Tom felt this was a route worth trying. He was right on target. Sangakkara had been one of Ceylon's greatest Rugby players and had been the Rugby coach at the university for many years. He regaled Tom with stories of his younger playing days and later coaching days. Tom listened. A quick rapport developed, and a friendship began which was to be vital to the success of the HOPE mission at Kandy.

The two decided that an informal gathering of all of the participants in the Kandy phase of the HOPE program was long overdue. Tom insisted that he would host the evening at the Hotel Suisse and that it would be open house with no time limit. John outdid himself in preparing the Suisse for the occasion. Every imaginable type of local dish was prepared, and John even improvised a few new ones. All of his boys donned fresh whites, and his moustache never looked better nor his back straighter.

The physicians came in their European clothes, the Ceylonese women in their saris that always look so much more beautiful on them than they do on European women. Some brought along that international instrument—the guitar. Our original group had been supplemented not only by Tom and Judy but by Marty and Jean Kohn—an internist husband-and-wife team who had served *Hope* in many nations. It promised to be a lively evening.

It was quite a debut for Judy, who had suddenly found herself a hostess in the mountain city of Kandy instead of in an apartment on Park Avenue. The combination of arrak and other traditional local refreshments brought immediate relaxation, and in no time at all the hills were filled with the sound of music. It wasn't always pretty, but it was loud! It was the music of people who had found a common ground and a friendship that was to sustain them through many trials. What music could be better?

The morning sky was already streaked with light by the time the last guests had gone. Tom and Judy would rest well, knowing that all would go more smoothly now. And Mo could sleep, for she now knew that she was to have active help from Bibs and Dr. Sangakkara for Male and Lollie, two children who had been left at the hospital from the time they were one week old. Now they were past three, and were still living in the pediatric ward. Some days they had clothes on, other days they roamed about naked because of the shortage of gowns on the wards. They shared cribs with other children or lay on mats on the concrete floor during the cold and wet nights.

How they had survived until now was a miracle. There was considerable doubt that they had ever been outside of the building until Mo arrived on the scene. Any inquiry about them brought only a shrug of the shoulders or a disclaimer of responsibility. It would have been more easily understood were there no orphanages for their care. But there were such children's homes, and it required only that someone cared enough to see that the transfer was carried out. Male and Lollie became Mo's personal mission. She obtained little dresses and other clothing for them. She kept them clean so that their hair, which had been shaved off because of lice, could be allowed to grow back. As soon as it was long enough, the hair was tied with gaily colored ribbons, and the two neglected little girls soon became the envy of the ward. During her time off, Mo and the other nurses would take the children out into the sunshine and show them the wonders of the land around them. Birds, flowers and just plain green grass—all were greeted with squeals of delight. To the children, it was a suddenly discovered, wondrous world.

This night she had been assured that the children would be placed and would have a home of sorts in an orphanage nearby. At least they would have decent food, friends of their own age and a place to play. When the time came, they would be educated. Another small victory, it would seem, but it was these small victories each day that meant so much. The knowledge that we cared made others care. The idea that we suggested another way or another approach to life but did not dogmatically demand it made these small victories possible.

There were greater changes on the horizon now that the barriers came down. The house officers and the students had been growing restive under the archaic methods of teaching still being practiced in Ceylon. Bibs had brought about some changes, but his exposure to modern methods of medical education had been limited. We had to wait until we were asked, and now he asked. He wanted a revision of the curriculum at Kandy, and Marty and Jean Kohn were ready and waiting. Both had been involved in the curriculum studies and planning undertaken at Stanford University and were strong advocates of the new ways being adopted at home in medical education. Daily meetings began and long distance correspondence was initiated with their friends at the university. Tom joined in, as did others from *Hope* who were trained medical educators.

The changes came slowly, but they came. First was the

greater accent on bedside clinical teaching. More student participation in conferences came next. Students were given the opportunity to spend time on the ship in Colombo so as to be exposed to a full American approach, and coincidentally see what
it was like to work in a clean hospital. They were asked by Bibs
to write their candid appraisal of these experiences (which they
did) and to make equally candid suggestions to him in regard to
their own school (which they did not—this was too much to expect).

What was important was the introduction of the concept of
change, which was to grow into actual changes as the year went
on. Perhaps Kipling was not completely correct. It was still too
early to tell.

That progress and new ways were both possible was dramatically demonstrated at the dental school, the only one in the
country, which was located at Kandy. It is a young school and
the faculty was struggling to overcome the stigma of the method
of student selection. Those who were assigned to the dental
school came from the lowest seventy-five grades among the
three hundred students who were tested for admission to medical school. The result was a lack of self-esteem in relation to the
medical students which was quite unjustified. It was not unlike
the system of selection in our own country fifty or more years
ago, so we should not have been surprised to see it in Ceylon.

The faculty were few in number, equipment was lacking, but
dedication was not. The first interest of the dental faculty was in
the improvement of dentistry in Ceylon. The chairman of our
dental department on the *Hope*, Harry Kavanaugh—a soft-spo-
ken, gray-haired dentist from Detroit—was quick to detect this
sentiment. From the moment of his first visit with Dr. Dissanay-
ake, the dean of the dental school, he knew that Kandy must be
the focus of his concentration.

Harry never told anyone anything, but he constantly and persistently suggested. He sent all of his better teachers to Kandy
hoping not only to encourage the faculty and their students but

actually to take part in the teaching. His patience and dedication were unending.

The problems were many. Seven faculty members were responsible for one hundred students, and two of these teachers were on leave of absence during our tenure in Kandy. The faculty members were cooperative but knew very little about clinical dentistry. They were not trained to remove caries, were unable to prepare an adequate amalgam preparation, which is essential for even the most modest filling of a decayed tooth, or to satisfactorily remove a calculus (sometimes called a stone and commonly found in the salivary ducts). Despite this lack of adequate clinical background, some of the "better" students are sent abroad for advanced training. Little can come from building on a deficient foundation.

Harry found the students bright and anxious to learn. They had a much more friendly relationship with their instructors than did the medical students. They learned to be patient about their lack of equipment. Both available dental X-ray machines were broken for most of the year. At home there would have been violent complaints. In Kandy the dental patients were sent to the Kandy Hospital with unexposed dental film and a request that a picture be taken of a specific tooth, processed, and returned to the school. Films were badly taken and equally badly processed, as would be expected. One of our visiting professors wanted to write a note to the radiologist and request that if the film was unsatisfactory it should be retaken. An extra supply of film could be provided for this purpose. The dental instructor felt this could not be done for it would be misunderstood. Therefore work continued with or without proper preoperative X rays. Harry was receiving his first lesson in the Oriental technique of the avoidance of direct confrontation when faced with a problem.

One of the sights our dental volunteers will never forget was the race from the bus to the clinic by all of the male and female students. This race took place each day because there was not enough working equipment in the clinic for all of those assigned to it. Originally, only nine dental engines were functional. Eventually twenty-three were in good working order, thanks to one of our *Hope* dentists who trained a young instructor and two senior students in the technique of their repair.

The dental lights were repaired and considerable relocation of equipment was done. All of this is part of what we in *Hope* call education, for education must begin at the very bottom. Our teachers developed an esprit de corps at the dental school that could not have been anticipated. In the process, Harry developed a peptic ulcer; but, happy day, today he has recovered without incident.

Not all of their work was confined to repairing equipment. There were a number of dramatic cases and demonstrations of new surgical techniques. Jim Peltier, an oral surgeon from Louisiana, operated upon a young Sinhalese man of twenty-six. He had been unable to open his mouth for twenty-two years and had existed on a diet of liquid and gruel. His lower jaw joint had been frozen as a complication of an untreated middle ear infection. The Ceylonese resident physician assisted Jim in the surgery which created a false temporomandibular joint, at the angle of the jaw where the mouth opens just below and in front of the ear. Immediately following the surgery, the man was able to open his mouth.

The following day when Jim made ward rounds, he found his patient sleeping with two fingers placed in his mouth. He had told the nurse that he was so happy with the result, and since he had never been able to put two fingers in his mouth before, he felt he wanted to sleep that way. The poor creature was really still not certain that his jaw would not freeze again while he was asleep, and didn't want to take any chances. When it came time for him to leave the hospital, he wanted to demonstrate his gratitude to Doctor Peltier. A gift alone was not enough, so he lay prostrate on the floor of the dental clinic with his hands clasped in front of him, wailing and wishing with all the fervor and humility he possessed that Jim would be blessed with a long life.

This is why Tom and Judy had come thousands of miles from America to a hill overlooking Kandy Lake. *Hope* was at work in Ceylon, and fulfillment always followed closely after.

# CHAPTER 12

The Bible teaches that helping the deaf to hear, the blind to see and the dumb to speak is God's work. But despite the many who have dedicated their lives to carrying out His purpose of helping the helpless and handicapped, there are some who believe the children or their parents are being punished for some unknown sin. Others believe these people have a *right* to be helped. Mary Anna Morris, a tall and attractive blonde therapist, was one of those.

A trained audiologist and speech therapist, she was gentle and kind. When she first decided to join the *Hope* staff in Ceylon, many questioned her usefulness. Speech therapy in a foreign language? Impossible! Can you banish the taboos about hereditary defects in a strange culture? Impossible! Everything seemed so impossible that Mary Anna could hardly wait to try. She knew that the science of communication—whatever the culture, whatever the language—depended first on love and understanding. These she had in abundance. And quiet stubbornness, too. Add to these qualities a beauty inside and out, and one had the perfect handmaiden for the Lord's work in this far-off land.

At first, Mary Anna was discouraged. There was, of course, the normal confusion that plagued every other medical program.

Her otolaryngologist was immediately snatched up by the local physicians in the same specialty so that they could learn the operative techniques for treatment of their own deaf patients, mostly adults whose hearing loss was the result of a common illness, otosclerosis. This was an important technique to be demonstrated, to be sure, but Dr. Mary Lekas, just as much as Mary Anna, was most anxious to help the forgotten children.

We had long known from experience in other nations and even at home that children with unrecognized deafness are frequently labeled as mentally retarded. Once labeled, they were quietly forgotten. Those who care for these children frequently are nonprofessionals who do not recognize that they may be dealing with a highly intelligent but deaf youngster. Where medical personnel already feel overburdened, concentration is inevitably centered upon those who are "treatable," and even more significantly those who are the most readily and easily treatable.

Mary Anna discovered that often the ear, nose and throat specialists in Colombo did not even know of the facilities available to them. There were many schools and centers, but no coordination between them or even information available to tell of their existence. Physicians told her that it would be useless to test hearing among the schoolchildren, for even if they were found deficient, no hearing aids were available. Mary Anna found this to be untrue and, in fact, found hearing aids in more than ample supply. They were among the few items which could be brought into Ceylon without arbitrary duty.

Add to all of these problems that mastermind who solves all problems in Ceylon—the astrologer. When parents brought deaf or blind children to him seeking some answer, he would consult his charts and stars and advise the parents that the child's horoscope indicated that he would hear or see after a certain age. Buttressed by this belief, the affected youngster would never be brought to a physician or clinic. The family simply waited for the omen to materialize. Many local physicians had come to ac-

cept this, for although scientists by training, they too believed in
the "signs." Those who were not believers simply shrugged their
shoulders. "Why fight it?"

When the "wizardry" of Mary Lekas, the *Hope* lady who
cured the deaf with surgery was publicized, the deaf came to
the clinics by the hundreds. They came from all over the city
and from all over the island. The local physicians and ministries
who were supposed to be responsible for their care were
amazed at both the numbers of deaf and the confusion in caring
for them. Hundreds of these patients were inoperable, but they
were convinced that a miracle was within reach and refused to
believe the truth when they had to be turned away. In those
harried days Mary Anna reflected ruefully that "she would have
been in complete accord with the changing of the name of our
mission from HOPE to MAYBE."

For the first few weeks, Mary Anna confined herself to testing
and attempting some speech therapy on the ship, using ward
patients or clinic patients, to demonstrate what could be done.
While en route to Ceylon she had acquired a working vocabu-
lary in Sinhalese equal to the level of a four-year-old child. She
knew this would be enough to get started. She explained her approach to me.

"There is no one answer as to how it is done. To teach a person to perfect his use of a word, you must present the concept,
and the word of single sound he is to learn, then reward him
when he responds. The reward need only be a smile or praise or
some other sign of approval. In Ceylon they want to communicate so badly that they make an effort so intensive that language
is no longer a barrier.

"A typical example," she went on, "was one tiny brown girl
who came to learn to use the speech appliance with which she
had been fitted following cleft palate surgery. She learned
quickly, for she had no accompanying hearing defect. She returned to her village, now able to be understood, and had re-
hearsed all that she was going to tell them. She had been pretty

well shunted aside before, since she could not speak, and this was to be her chance to straighten out both her family and neighbors. First, she demanded her rights.

" 'We have only four chairs at home, and *I* never got one. My missy at *Hope* put *me* in a chair and she sat on the floor.' (I frequently kneel when working with small children so I can see their faces better—but I hadn't intended this as a lesson.) 'Further,' she said, 'my missy speaks *English*, but nobody around here has bothered to teach me any.'

"The next week, she proudly returned with her Sinhalese lesson translated into English (ruining the effect of it). She did so much talking about *Hope* that the neighbors who had never heard her speak before thought that she had completed her speech therapy in a week's time.

"I musn't forget to mention," Mary Anna added, "that children are much the same everywhere. At home they used to bring me bunches of daisies to show their gratitude. This little girl, like the others, brings a handful of freshly picked orchids each time she comes for a lesson."

Mary Anna had also had the good fortune to meet Mr. Cooray, the principal of the Mt. Lavinia School for the Deaf. He was a charming man, and a real go-getter. He had been trained in the techniques of educating the deaf in Australia. Upon his return to Ceylon he either trained or partially trained some twenty teachers. The school itself was run on a shoestring, but was a functioning example of what could be done with meager resources if pride, initiative and willingness to work are present. Cooray visited the ship every moment he was free and personally extended invitations to everyone to visit his school. He wanted suggestions, improvements in record keeping, lectures to his teachers, immunizations for the children, or anything that would involve people in the problems of helping these youngsters. He called Mary Anna almost every morning at precisely six thirty with new ideas and suggestions.

She soon became as interested in involving others in the

school as he was. Everywhere she went she heard the tale, "Ceylon is an underdeveloped country. We don't have special schools and equipment here such as you have in the United States." She began to feel like a one-woman Chamber of Commerce, because her standard reply became: "Come with me to the School for the Deaf. You'll see what your own people have done without a great deal of money or expensive equipment."

The persistence of one can sometimes move a nation. Mary Anna was determined and gathered together a small delegation to pay a visit on the national director of social services, whose department controlled the schools for the deaf. The purpose of the visit initially was to arrange for counterparts for us to train in the technique of audiology. In Ceylon, nothing is ever accomplished with only one meeting; but after several at which gallons of tea were consumed, instead of counterparts our staff was drawn into a plan that would offer something for all of the schools for the deaf.

The director explained that the outstation schools were frequently little more than residential homes where the children have literally been put away. The schools were under the direction of the department of education, but the assigned teachers had no training, for the deaf were simply considered untrainable. Petty jealousies and ethnic differences further divided the schools in much the same manner as they had divided the wards in the leprosarium.

Mary Anna suggested a training seminar for teachers of the deaf, cosponsored by the Department of Social Services and the National Council for the Deaf. There was immediate agreement on the merits of the idea but some doubts as to whether it could be carried out. The three affected ministries—Social Service, Education, and Health—had never cooperated in a project before. But who could turn down the idea of this pretty blonde?

To everyone's surprise, many resources were discovered. The local physicians were proud and anxious to participate in giving lectures and attending discussions. The trained teachers of the deaf, who numbered only five, had all received some training abroad and gave demonstrations and led discussions. Significantly they received deserved recognition of their special skills from those outside the deaf community for the first time. Representatives from the various ministries participated and, above all, listened themselves. *Hope* physicians, nurses and paramedical specialists participated throughout.

The seminar lasted eight days and was well attended. There was considerable group involvement, which could have been construed as disorder by one not recognizing it as enthusiasm. People kept jumping to their feet and offering spontaneous translations of comments, or asked whatever questions popped into their minds. Everyone learned a great deal. One of Colombo's leading specialists even discovered there was more than one school for the deaf in Ceylon. For years he had been telling patients: "Well, it's no use. There is only one school for the deaf in Ceylon and the waiting list is so long. . . ." There was no waiting list at all.

Unbelievably, we were told this was the first time that training of the kind discussed at the seminar was to be offered on local soil. Just the saving in hard-to-find currency required to send students abroad would be a considerable benefit. Of even more importance was the hope that the combined effort by the three ministries would serve as an example and lesson in cooperation to the competitive bureaucracies that govern this land.

Next on the agenda was to involve the community further and make clear to the parents and children alike that something concrete was really going to be done. The Mount Lavinia School for the Deaf was the springboard. The principal had a plethora of ideas that he had never been able to implement because of lack of interest and support.

A preschool nursery was begun at Mount Lavinia as a pilot program, with two young Ceylonese teachers working together with an American volunteer teacher of the deaf and Mary Anna. Within a matter of months, they had prepared eight children to enter the school for the deaf as regular students. A small dent, perhaps, but a sincere demonstration that the children should be diagnosed and helped early. These youngsters had been fitted with hearing aids and trained in their maintenance and use. They had acquired the basic concepts necessary for the beginning of "deaf" education. Their parents had received consistent counseling, and three sets of parents had shown the necessary leadership qualities to form the core of a conscientious parents' group. This is a necessity in training the deaf. The teachers had gained skill and experience in handling young children. The principal of the school presented to his board of directors a request for necessary support to establish a regular preschool program, using the success of this program as an example. A whole generation of handicapped was to be given hope.

Mary Anna, day in and day out, conducted hearing aid evaluations and tirelessly preached the necessity of follow-up, an assurance that the aids were used properly and batteries replaced regularly. A small child can become frustrated and discouraged so easily when unable to understand mechanical failures. A taste of sound and then a return to silence would have been disastrous. One teacher was taught the technique of making ear molds for hearing aids, and sufficient materials and equipment were obtained so that every child in the Mt. Lavinia School could be provided with an aid. The technician was permitted to make some for private individuals as well so that the profit earned could be plowed back into purchasing more materials.

The *Hope* Public Health team conducted physical examinations on all of the children and a workable system of medical records was devised. The health educator, nutritionist and public health nurses spent hours working with the matrons and the school's teachers. Emphasis was repeatedly placed upon the need for the team approach here in these schools as well as in every aspect of medicine.

The maritime crew of the *Hope* became involved as well. Funds were needed for a sound-treated room where hearing

could be tested properly after the ship left. The crew decided to
give a benefit dance and use the proceeds for a variety of proj-
ects, including the sound-treated room. The room was constructed locally with available materials, a lesson which removed
still another excuse for neglect. The opening ceremonies were
held prior to our sailing, and the principal proudly unveiled a
plaque on the wall which read, "Donated by the Crew of the
S. S. *Hope.*" It was his surprise to us. The British High Commis-
sioner had been so impressed with the combined effort that he
donated an audiometer—the instrument which is required to
test hearing. There was even money left over, and with this the
school established a hearing-aid-battery fund so that the poor
children could be supplied with batteries that they would otherwise be unable to buy.

This kind of activity did not stop with the one school. With a
little prodding from some proud but persistent Hopies, the principal and teachers of the Mt. Lavinia School passed on to the
directors of other schools all of the techniques which they had
acquired, from professional skills to fund raising.

The schools for the deaf and the blind became a great source
of help to the *Hope* staff as well. When morale on the ship was
low, many of those staff members who were off for the day
would arrange to join Mary Anna for a visit to "her schools."
Her favorites for these visiting days were the Ratmalana School
for the Deaf, the Ragama School for the Deaf and Blind, and
the Good Shepherd Convent. These schools were in the country,
clean, airy and cheerful. Now, too, they were filled with hope.

The children themselves did all of the work around the buildings and grounds, and grew sufficient vegetables for their own
consumption. They kept chickens and occasionally one would
see a rather bony cow. They kept their own quarters clean and
took care of their own belongings. Each time the children knew
visitors were coming, they would prepare an entertainment and
were delighted with and proud of their performances.

The deaf children did a series of dances to the unheard beat of native drums standing on the floor, and the teachers explained that the beat was picked up through the acute sensory perception in the feet—simply from the vibrations. Their rhythm was perfect.

The blind children sang to the audience they could not see. Their favorite rendition of the *Hope* staffers was "America the Beautiful," and it never failed to bring tears to every eye. It seemed such a pity that the Ceylonese people themselves rarely visited these institutions, for it was so important to these children to know that someone cared. We did our best to invite Ceylonese colleagues and students along but often wonder whether they continued to visit these children after we left. I don't see how they could fail to, for the faces of the children are irresistible.

The blind students at the Ragama School were taught by a young woman of twenty-six called Gertrude, who was an orphan, and had been living at the school since she was a small child. She dressed in a crisp, neat frock and never wore any shoes. She had never owned a pair. Gertrude used Sinhalese in the classroom, although she spoke the other local languages. She spoke English as well, a rather remarkable achievement for an orphaned child in a country in which illiteracy had been attacked only in recent years. The students loved her and were inspired by her affection and attention. More than that, she could identify with them, for she too was totally blind and had been all of her life.

Her fondest hope was that her application for care on board the ship would be accepted, for like so many others in Ceylon she had come to believe that the *Hope* doctors could perform miracles. One day her prayers were answered and she was given an appointment at the screening clinic in Colombo so it could be determined whether to admit her to the ship as a patient. She returned to Ragama smiling, and all who knew her felt a sudden uplift. She sensed it, although she could not see it, and she explained.

"I visited the *Hope* doctor today, but he told me that nothing could be done to restore my vision. You wonder why I'm happy. It's not because of the bad news; but the doctor sat down with me and gave me and me alone fifteen minutes of his time to explain why I could not be helped. Can you imagine, out of his busy morning. I'll never forget his kindness."

I envied our quiet, wonderful Mary Anna Morris. I envied the satisfaction she must have felt for what she had started and accomplished in the support of these few Ceylonese teachers who had desperately attempted to get help and attention for their charges. While so many of our own young men and women are lamenting the lack of compassion in the world, this young lady had done something about it. Thanks to her, many of the deaf will hear, some of the blind will see, and the dumb will speak.

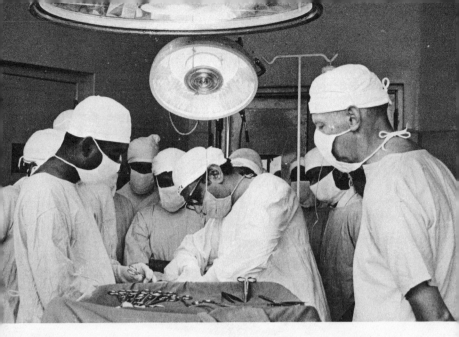

ABOVE: Dr. Earl Boehme works with counterparts in the operating theater of Kandy General Hospital. By working closely together in this manner, American doctors are able to teach local counterparts the latest American medical techniques. BELOW: Grace Tucker helps serve breakfast in a ward of the Kandy General Hospital.

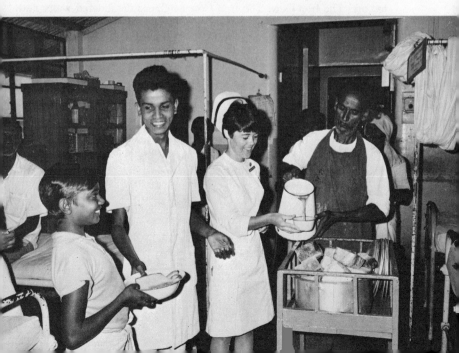

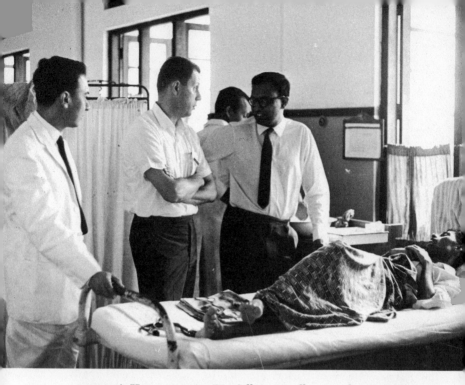

ABOVE: A HOPE surgeon, Dr. Gilbert Mueller, Jr., discusses the progress of a patient with several counterparts in Kandy General Hospital. BELOW: The Iron Cow. The Iron Cow combines desalinated water and dried milk to make whole milk. This milk is used aboard the hospital ship as a part of its program in nutrition.

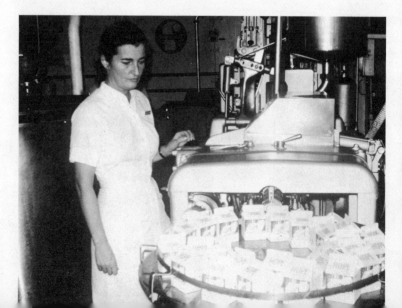

HOPE personnel were continually surprised by the excitement generated by their distribution of small cartons of milk as part of a pilot nutrition program. These cartons were not immediately drunk, but were carried home by the children they were given to, to be shared by the entire family.

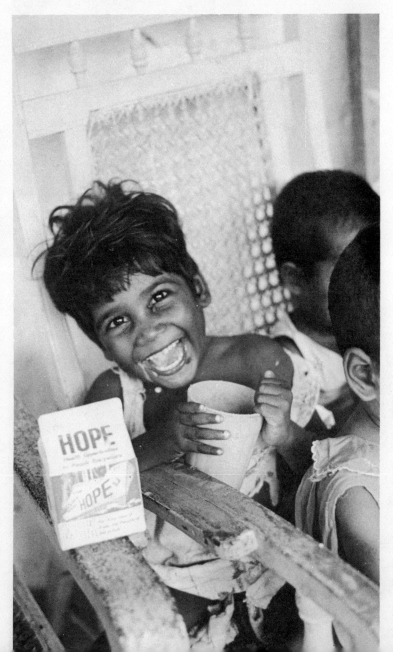

ABOVE: Mo Gallagher and Inge Hansen wish "Ayubowan" (respectful greetings) to pediatric patients. BELOW: A HOPE nurse, Mary Louise Foltz, and her Ceylonese counterpart check on a patient in Kandy General Hospital.

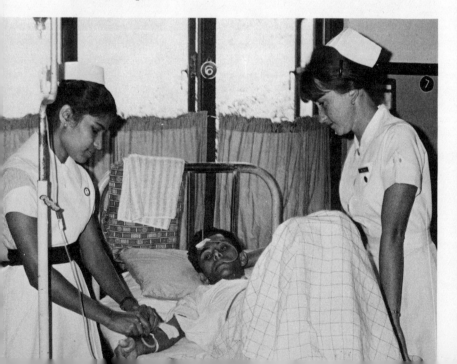

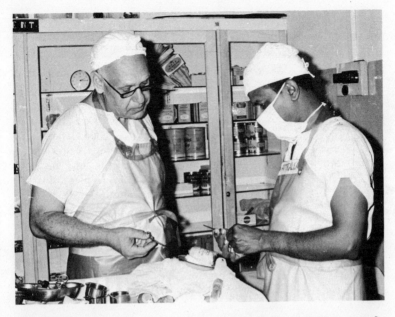

ABOVE: Dr. Henry Bodner, a urologist aboard the S.S. *Hope*, works with his Ceylonese counterpart in the Kandy General Hospital. BELOW: Mary Lou Roppe and her counterpart talk with a young patient in the Thoracic Surgical ward of Colombo General Hospital.

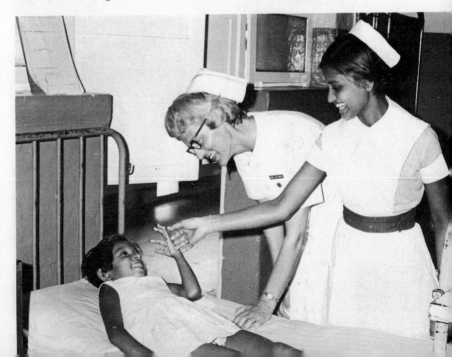

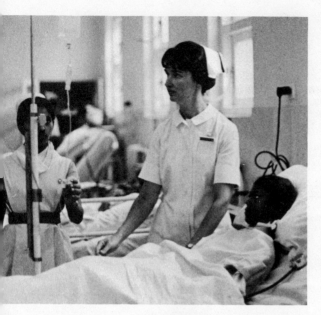

Diana Stafford and her counterpart check on a patient in the new Intensive Care Unit at Colombo General Hospital. HOPE was instrumental in the development of this unit.

Dr. Jo Ann Cornet and her counterpart examine a patient at Lady Ridgeway Hospital.

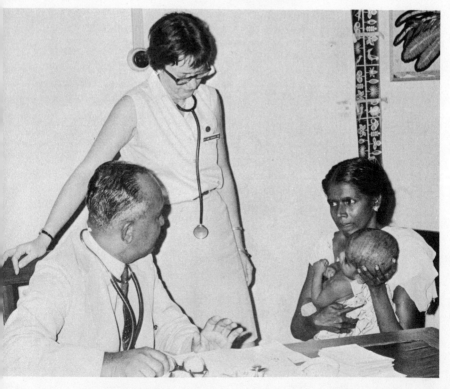

Vivian Crosswhite and her counterpart are pleased with a patient's progress. This is the Physiotherapy Clinic at Lady Ridgeway Hospital.

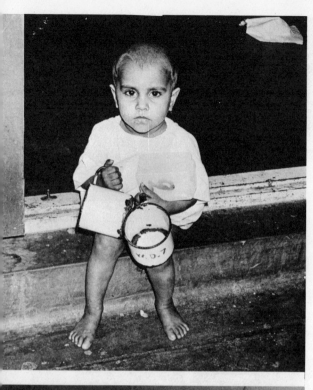

Little children like this one are the concern of HOPE, for if they can be kept healthy today they can become productive members of society in the future.

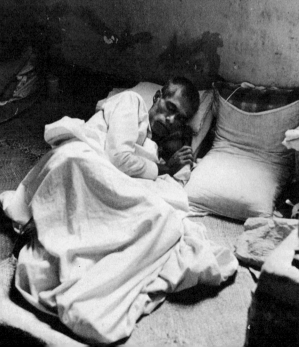

This man must sleep on the floor of an overcrowded hospital.

ABOVE: This is one of the wards painted by HOPE in the Leprosy Hospital. BELOW: George White, officers' messman aboard the hospital ship, gives a glass of milk to one of a group of children at the Prithipura Home for the mentally retarded.

RIGHT: Dave Godley, a student summer volunteer on the ship, works with students of the Maradana School on clean-up day.
BELOW: Judy Berner works with her Ceylonese counterpart in the Thoracic Intensive Care Unit of Colombo General Hospital. HOPE was instrumental in the development of this unit.

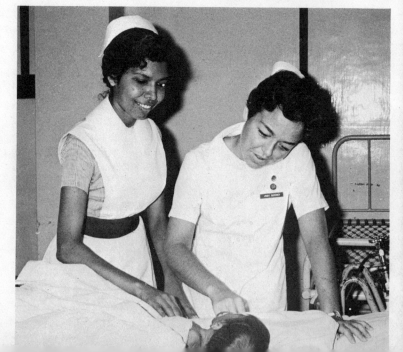

ABOVE: Mrs. Walsh and Bill McDiarmid, a student summer volunteer, share smiles with students at The School for the Deaf at Ratmalana. BELOW: Judy Golbuff visits a Ceylonese family in the Pittakotte area as part of a HOPE Public Health program.

RIGHT: Dr. John R. Paul and Patrick McGreal talk with students at the Prithipura Home for the mentally retarded. BELOW: John Walsh (top right), a student summer volunteer with HOPE, works with students during a clean-up day at the Maradana School. John is the son of Dr. William B. Walsh.

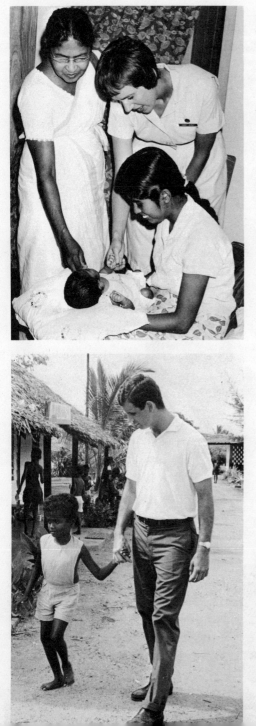

Miss Peggy Emrey, a nurse-midwife, makes a home visit to one of her patients. The baby was born at home and delivered by a midwife whom Peggy had trained. Only two days before the baby was born, Peggy had given a class in mouth-to-mouth resuscitation. The baby was born not breathing and was revived by the midwife.

John Baker, a student summer volunteer with HOPE, walks hand in hand with a young Ceylonese boy at the Prithipura Home for the mentally retarded.

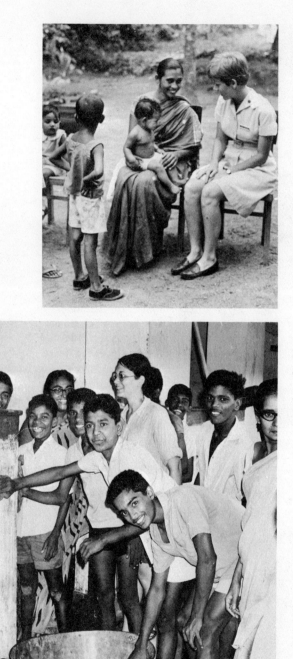

A HOPE nurse, Nancy Brandes, talks with Ceylonese mothers about their children's health.

Leslie Kron at the Maradana School in Ceylon. Leslie's tragic death was on July 19, 1968.

Elephants were included in the departure ceremonies of the S.S. *Hope*.

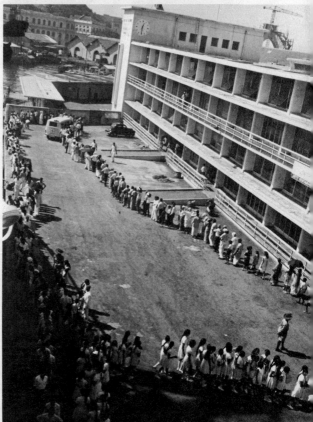

Thousands line up to tour the white hospital ship before its departure from Ceylon.

A young Ceylonese boy pauses to take a last look at the white hospital ship *Hope*. Having had polio several years earlier, he was able to walk only after surgical treatment and bracing received on the ship.

# CHAPTER 13

Each day that passed brought its small successes, a better understanding of our Ceylonese colleagues—and exhaustion. Working, teaching and the constant battle of man against disease and neglect can be spiritually wearing. Our staff gradually discovered means of trying to forget their daily problems, looking forward to that occasional day or weekend when they could leave Colombo. One of the favorite hideaways was in Hikkaduwa, some ninety miles down the coast from Colombo.

Here was a different world. The Coral Gardens Hotel became *Hope* headquarters away from home. It was only on a rare occasion that a Poya Day went by without one of our staff swimming, snorkeling or just relaxing with Ceylonese friends. It was on this kind of visit that we learned really to know some of our colleagues. They, too, were so relaxed when away from Colombo that their guard was down and they would talk of their dreams and hopes for the future.

The hotel was in a beautiful setting by the sea. Depending upon the season, one could snorkel at will or not go near the water at all. During the monsoon the winds were high and the water rough. It was not unusual at these times to see rising waves cover the roads through some of the seaside villages. At the barrier reef where the waves converging from two directions met, the swirl and whirlpool made swimming impossible. Ten-foot breakers sometimes reached the shore, coming dangerously close to the hotel.

No one ever seemed to worry, however, so I would suppose none ever actually did reach the hotel itself. The first floor rooms with lanais offered little security to the visitor, so during the stormy season all *Hope* staffers preferred the second-floor rooms with outside balconies. They were not a bit farther away from the water, but they seemed safer. You could spend the entire day enthralled watching the myriad flocks of seagulls gracefully circle, then sweep down into the water, never failing to come up with a fish. Native fishermen sat patiently in handmade outriggers which looked as if they could not possibly survive the strength and the fury of the sea. They stayed within the reef and waited for the proper time and then rowed quickly out to the sea beyond to do their day's fishing. None stayed out more than half an hour, but in that time the catch was ample.

There were many small villages around, with a devil dance as the local specialty. The Hindu population in this area was deeply religious and felt that serious illness was the result of a patient being seized by evil spirits. Dancers had to be hired and a precise ritual performed to exorcise the devils within. It was refreshing to see people who believed strongly in something— their form of prayer—attempting such a ceremony. If it worked, all was well. If it did not, there was no loss of faith; exorcism would be attempted again later, with a different approach being used to drive out the evil spirits.

One particular evening the rites were to be held in a small village nearby. After a short drive and a walk up a footpath, we were at the site of the ceremony. It was held in the yard area behind a house, and all of the relatives and neighbors had gathered. An area in the yard had been swept clean, and two coconut palm altars erected there. On one of the altars was a crude painting of the monkey god.

The patient, a young woman dressed in a beautiful white cotton sari, lay on a white pallet on the porch, her head propped on her arm, the better to see the proceedings. She was suffering from a long-standing disease and sometimes cried for long periods. She also had convulsions, so possibly she was epileptic. No one really knew of a diagnosis. This was not important to the villagers anyway; if the dance worked she would be cured. From the surrounding jungle, drums started to beat and suddenly two male dancers appeared in the center of the ring. They were dressed in white sarongs with red, black and white tops covering their chests. They wore headdresses of palm fronds which rose high above their heads and made them look like the medicine man portrayed so often in our own Westerns on television.

They started chanting and dancing to the beat of the drums. All watched breathless as the men moved faster and faster, round and round the picture of the monkey god and dancing occasionally toward the girl. They carried palm torches, which they juggled and periodically powdered with a chemical substance to make them throw flame in all directions. This continued for an hour and was only the beginning. During the ritual an ample supply of arrak, a coconut liquor, was supplied for the dancers so that they would not lose their frenzy or mood of entreaty to the monkey god.

The dance continued all night, and gradually built to a climax when the dancers donned the devil masks, breathing fire from their painted mouths. At that moment the patient joined the dance. In the eyes of the Westerner, primitive perhaps. But, whatever the effect on her condition, we were impressed with the evidence of such deep and implicit faith in someone or something stronger than man himself.

The more one remained in Ceylon, the more one wondered about the traditional importance of these beliefs. The next day while en route back to Colombo, we tossed theories back and forth. Some were tolerant, others were not. So much revolved around the belief in the predestiny of man and the pathways planned for him by the stars and the planets. In Ceylon almost 80 percent of the marriages are planned by parents who look for a mate for their child according to the horoscope. It is not unusual to see an eligible partner described in a newspaper advertisement, stating the age, dowry and other details. Anyone who replies to the ad is advised to bring his horoscope with him. Amulets and other types of charms are worn to ward off sickness and evil. This is frequently done on the advice of an astrologer who has told the wearer that a dominant planet may threaten his or her well-being, and this evil can be warded off only by the powerful presence of the amulet.

Palmists and astrologers were given ample opportunity to demonstrate their wisdom and power by curious *Hope* staffers. To some, not infrequently the coincidental accuracy of recounting an experience of the past, which could not have been known by the astrologist, created at least a reasonable belief. It was a little nerve-racking to find that they were either accurate or that we lead lives so similar to our fellow humans that a high percentage of guesses could be correct.

But in Ceylon there were no greater demonstrators of faith than the fire walkers. Kolonnawa Village, which is near Colombo, had a ceremony almost weekly. As a little warm-up to fire walking, it was not uncommon to view other sacrificials who pierced their bodies with needles or suspended themselves from metal hooks driven through their skin. Others pulled carts with ropes extending from hooks beneath their skin. Each ceremony was similar except that the number of fire walkers varied from a dozen up to seventy-five. They could be children of ten and men of seventy. The reason? Penance, perhaps, or self-punishment or a demonstration of gratitude to the Hindu God of Kataragama. Many Buddhists continue to take part in these ceremonies because the Hindu deities for these rites, Vishnu and the God of Kataragama, are recognized by Buddhists as well.

We who thought we were reinforcing twentieth century medicine in Ceylon were understandably skeptical. I doubt, therefore, that any *Hope* staff member missed a fire-walking rite. The local believers encouraged our attendance, even sent announcements to the ship whenever a ceremony was scheduled. They permitted us to conduct any type of investigation we desired without any feeling of offense or resentment. We tested the heat of the coals, one thousand degrees fahrenheit. We examined the feet of the fire walkers before and after their exercise, and were permitted to take surgical skin biopsies of the soles of the feet to determine if they were protected in any way or were unusually calloused. No one ever found even the most remote skin change, evidence of a burn or anything other than normal skin.

It was shortly after our return from Hikkaduwa that we went to our first fire-walking ceremony. As we approached Kolonnawa Village, we could already hear the music from the flutes and the drums. The ceremony was started early in the evening and lasted most of the night. Fronds of margosa decorated the doorway of a house in the village, flowers were everywhere and alms to the Hindu Gods were laid out in the courtyard of the house. Buddhist flags were flying and there was a small shrine set up with smoking incense. The crowd watched everything with a deep and reverent silence.

On this occasion there was also to be skin piercing. Those who were to experience this worked themselves up into a hypnotic state by frenzied dancing to the accompaniment of drums beaten by what seemed like the fury of a thousand hands. The man in charge then stood before those dancers who were to have their skin pierced by skewers. They knelt motionless, covered with sacred ash, and each had the rough skewers driven through both cheeks. None cried out, none fainted and none visibly bled. One man had hooks driven into his lower back and thighs and then was suspended into the air, holding his own body weight only with the strength of his skin. Still no cry. And the music continued. And the coals for the fire walking continued to burn.

It was hours later that the dancers, who seemed never to stop, circled the burning coals. The red-hot pathway was about twenty to thirty feet long, although it could well have been that many miles were I one of the faithful. Suddenly the first of them started through, swaying, not hurrying, in a trance. Others followed, some returning two or three times, with never a sign of pain. For the first time I understood that the Buddhist immolations in Vietnam might not be to protest the war, but a promise of penance made long years before. A stunning demonstration, and the only explanation for these fire walkers is downright Faith.

Ceylon has many holy men who also claim a spiritual knowledge of science. One wrote us his explanation of these phenomena and asked that we distribute it on the ship.

Sir:
  With humble apoligies, I crave your pardon to put forward my research findings to those interested in your *"Hope"* ship.
  1. A Ceylonese nurse trainee (a niece of mine) brought to my notice that certain doctors in your ship had shown some interest in fire walking and such occult experiences. This letter is a result of it.
  2. Westerners are easily mislead by mysticism of the east, especially by theorists and quacks who sometimes have developed powers without any knowledge of hidden scientific principles.
  3. Anesthesia, insensibility to pain or pleasure, catalepsy and other changes in the body chemistry could be well understood through hypnosis which could be brought about in various ways like hetero-suggestion and auto-suggestion. The so-called "God believers" only bring about a state of self hypnosis by a process of faith, ritualism, etc. and arouse their latent forces in the body creating various spiritual phenomena. Of course the ignorant believers attribute it to various gods according to their beliefs which are deep seated in their subconscious minds. Fire walking and such things are a common feature in various religions like Hinduism, Islam and even among jungle tribes. Fire walkers only walk on burnt sprinkled wood charcoal, but no such God believer would dare to walk on heated iron sheets. Hetero-hyp-

nosis and auto-hypnosis has provided wonderful, unbelievable powers to certain practitioners. Even today child deliveries, painless tooth extractions and such things have been performed through hypnosis. During the war time, emergency operations had been done through hypnosis only. Stoppage of blood oozing, creation of blisters (as if burnt by a candle) have been brought about through hypnosis. No wonder today modern medical science attribute that about 70% of diseases are caused by mental attitudes.

4. It is said that suggestion oversteps the bounds of medical treatment. Modern science psychology has only limited knowledge of the mind and its forces which is limited to the *conscious* and *sub-conscious* minds. Only spiritual yoga or religious philosophy could explain the super-conscious mind which is the finest and the most powerful state in the body and in the universe. This super-conscious mind or state is the God all knowing, all powerful and all pervading, creator, preserver and destructor of the body and the universe . . . will give a better explanation of it.

5. We have seen sometimes Professor Surgeons have failed in long normal operations, which of course they term as medical misadventure and pass it off. Also there are instances where their Professors have advised to stand an operation, such ailments have been cured by a simple Yoga physical exercise or a small charm or a light indigenous decoration. We have to admit that in spite of wonderful modern researches in medicine, etc., no science is still a hundred per cent correct in this changing world. Any discovery is such that the only HOPE of the world of humanity lies in the discovery of this super-conscious mind or state, the origin of all things.

6. On religions—Theorists of various religions criticize each other and try to explain their superiority over others. It is like the blind trying to describe the elephant or the sun. Truth is one . . . call it by different names. The means of approach and the methods of understanding the goal appear to differ. Failure to understand the hidden meanings of the Bible, Buddhism, Islamism, Hinduism have brought about all chaos among the believers. Jesus, Buddha, other yogis, saints, etc. all had developed mass hypnotic powers and utilised it when it was necessary to impress people. Many are instances from the Bible etc. For example—If one travels from Washington to California (a) by

foot, (b) by cycle, (c) by car, (d) by train, (e) by plane, the goal
is California by whatever way one may go. Description of the
route is the same, but it varies according to the education or
wisdom of the traveler. That is why similar stories or parables,
etc. are found in Christianity, Buddhism, Hinduism, Yoga, etc.
Every religion shows the particular path a saint has followed to
attain eternal bliss couched in weird and poetic language, but
lusty foolish devotees misunderstand, mistranslate the secret
doctrines and degrade and destroy humanity in the name of religions. Environmental conditions and the passage of time have
all changed the originality of all religions. While paying my respects to all religions and science, I think the safest and the most reliable path to emancipation or liberation lies in Buddhism in the
*Four Noble Truths.*

I hope sincerely that long life, happiness and enlightenment
may come to all in S. S. HOPE through their noble and sacrific-
ing efforts in healing and relieving the sufferings of the sick.

While remembering that an atom of practice is worth more
than tons of theory, I shall stop with sincere regards and humble apologies to all volunteer healers of the missionary ship S. S.
HOPE.

I remain,

> Yours truly,
> K. Samaraweera.

I discussed these conclusions with our psychiatrist, Phil Heersema, who had been vitally interested in the local attitudes toward psychiatry, particularly in view of these deep religious beliefs. He was especially interested in the general attitude of the
Ceylonese population toward mental illness. What would be
their level of sophistication in the eyes of American or British
psychiatry, the degree of transition from witchcraft, voodoo and
mystical practices to scientific medicine? What advances could
be promoted for the goal of sound psychological healing?

He was pleasantly surprised with what he had found. The
doctors were conscientious and making a real effort. They had
an impersonal attitude toward their patient which was born of
an innate shyness in physician and patient alike. He advised me
that "all of the psychiatrist-physicians" in Ceylon were conver-

sant with the practices of "local doctors," meaning their various forms of mystical rites and exorcism, devil dances, the use of charms and amulets. Most patients admitted to the hospital wore such ornaments and no attempt was made to forbid them nor to downgrade the practice itself, which spoke well for the kindliness of the physicians and the positive approach to their patients.

"To me," Phil said, "the outstanding characteristic of Ceylon as a whole was the rather gentle containment of many inevitable frustrations and despairs resulting from overpopulation, illiteracy (though comparatively low), poverty and the inequity of the haves and the have-nots.

"The acceptance of fate, with some help from the betel nut and its narcotic qualities, mystic healing, and abiding faith in the Buddhist (or Hindu) philosophy marks the Ceylonese (Sinhalese and Tamils) as an outwardly passive people. But they have great pride in their heritage (and correctly so) and if this pride of heritage is diminished or denigrated, a process of passive resistance ensues which transcends and obliterates any obvious benefits at hand.

"Does this hold true among the educated? Would this manifest itself as a passive resistance among some of those specialists who seem almost afraid to work with us? Perhaps it is we who are misunderstanding or frustrating them."

"Of course," said another listener, "that's not only possible but likely. This obtains with any people with a lineage of centuries and may well account for the resentment toward America and its aid abroad. This is why Hope succeeds in great part. It is a soft and individual approach. A suggestive or adjunctive technique of a person-to-person relationship. Those of our staff who have problems would likely be the same ones who would have a 'prima donna' problem in their own school, community or hospital at home."

Phil resumed, "The formula is simple. 'If I have enough sophistication and stamina to have survived twenty centuries, why should I be overwhelmed with gratitude or adopt without question the teachings of these foreigners?' Teaching is the employment of techniques used with children. 'Maybe you could do it this way. . . .' and NOT 'That's all wrong, watch me.'

"The substitution of caste for effort is bound to occur if the individual does not make constant examination of his motives and drives. This is apparent in Ceylon in the efforts comparatively extended by the Tamils (one fifth of the population and only one half of whom are allowed to vote) and the Sinhalese (more than two thirds of the population, all allowed to vote). The latter have a far richer and longer-recorded history and make capital thereof. It sounds a little bit like home, doesn't it?

"But," Phil went on, "to get now to the original point of discussion which I had to preface briefly, you ask about the firewalking ritual. This is by far the most dramatic demonstration of the pride of tradition, devotion, cohesion and faith. It is preceded in my opinion by the induction of a mild trance—autohypnosis—with no visible or photographic evidence of burns, blistering or scarring . . . a situation which is almost as baffling after witnessing the ritual as it is beforehand. I was in close communication with the two leaders of last night's ritual throughout the entire five hours, from lighting the bonfire to the walking. As a result, I am fully satisfied that this is not a display put on by psychotic misfits, but rather a ritual exercised only by the fit, sane devotee, enraptured though he may be by the role he has been chosen to perform, and the quasi-hypnotic state which resulted from that role.

"That remarkable ritual, and the act of the suspension by six hooks inserted into the skin of the back and the thighs of the devotee as well, serves to bring the mystical past of these people into the social present and scientific purview of modern-day observers with many unanswered questions, but essentially mutual tolerance and respect."

I thought for a moment and reflected upon the observations of the Holy Man, Kithsena Samaraweera, together with those of our twentieth century psychiatrist. In conclusion, they were not vastly different but only by the pathway, as our Buddhist friend had indicated. Perhaps we were not too far apart after all. Maybe someday the twain . . . ?

# CHAPTER 14

Since 1960 Project HOPE has provided an opportunity for young men and women of college age, as well as medical students on electives, the chance to help others within the "establishment" of the *Hope* ship. We have far more applicants than we can possibly take, and they come from everywhere in the nation and from every background. Some are wealthy, some poor, but all have that common spirit of wanting to learn, help, do; not to destroy. They have not been headlined in the magazines or the press, for theirs has been a good and constructive work, of which we all can be proud.

Over the years we have had students from Princeton, Harvard, Yale, Columbia, Trinity, University of North Carolina, University of California, Rollins, University of Wisconsin, University of Iowa, Texas A. and M., Wayne State University, U.C.L.A., Smith, George Washington University and others. A wide spectrum. We have never had a disappointing performance from any one of them, and all returned to the United States richer for their participation. This year in Ceylon our young Hopies were like the others who had come to us in the summer months.

When the college group arrived in Colombo, the ship had already been in port about two months. Their appearance, as always, was like a transfusion for the entire staff. Young, eager and filled with an undefinable type of spirit, they were ushered aboard by Bill Walsh, Jr., just graduated from Trinity College and charged with the responsibility of the student program. His group was laden down with a minimum of clothing but a maximum of collateral equipment such as guitars, books for required summer reading, record players and the usual variety of gear carried everywhere by men and women of their age.

They were packed into quarters well belowdecks, six to a room. Off came the traveling clothes and on went the shorts and dungarees, for they had come prepared to work. The inexhaustible energy of the young was such that, despite an all-day and all-night flight, sleep was the farthest thing from their minds. Their route had been from New York to London, Athens, Kuwait, Bombay, and finally to Colombo—almost twenty solid hours in the air—topped off by the hot and wild ride from the Colombo airport to dockside. Yet, here they were bright-eyed and ready to go.

Bill, with the help of his younger brother John, conducted an afternoon briefing on the philosophy of the student programs. Both of these young men had been participating for years, equally as a result of their own desire and a degree of influence as members of the Walsh family. The presentation was direct and simple. "You are a part of something very important. You are here because you chose to volunteer and each of you has paid your own expenses to get here. You will not be paid, but you will be expected to work seven days a week and as many hours each day as you are asked. You will have the opportunity to plan some of your own programs, for there is so much to do we cannot do it all, and we want to take advantage of the best talents of each of you."

"What about some of the older doctors?" inquired Gary Lewis, a student from North Carolina. "A couple of them gave us that knowing 'here come the delinquents look.' Do they know anything about the student program?"

"Most of them do, but remember they have all had a pretty good dose of the daily stories on student rebellions at home. Some of them may be a bit skeptical about why we're here and what we can accomplish."

"Right," chimed in Bear Baker, a Princeton graduate who had served a summer in Nicaragua. "This means we have a double job to perform. First the assignments we have to help the Ceylonese. Second, making some of these men realize that all of this generation isn't from hunger."

"Another point," Bill added, "is to remember that the local press has reprinted just about everything bad that they can about the students at home and how we are bent on destroying the system. They'll watch everything you do, and listen to every word you say, and don't be surprised to see your accomplishments, if that is what we can call them, in the daily paper.

"One of the most important points to remember is to be yourself. Don't pretend and don't patronize. Part of our job is to let the Ceylonese see for themselves exactly what we are. We want to make friends with their students and learn what they are. We want to understand something about the people of our own age group who will be responsible for running the world of tomorrow. The initiative is going to have to be ours, because the Ceylonese are basically a shy and polite people. But by initiative please understand—I don't mean overly aggressive."

Questions, answers, discussions lasted the entire afternoon. Other members of the staff were introduced and outlined their thoughts and plans. Most of the time was given to the health educator and the public health group, for it was in this area that the summer students were to make their greatest contribution. They listened avidly as the possibilities for participation were presented to them. Work at the leprosarium—to a group who previously believed a leper was an untouchable; development of a recreation and physical education program at the jail—the athletes of the group stirred with interest; participation in the milk distribution program at the schools; work with the children at the schools for the blind and the deaf; the possibility of a special project all their own at an elementary school in a ghetto area of Colombo, the Maradana School; aiding in the audiovisual education programs planned by the health educator; participation in home visits with the public health nurses, not only to make notes but to see and learn how to help the hopeless. The opportunities were unlimited.

The boys found it difficult to believe that the group around them had the temerity to tackle so much and more. But Nancy Brandes, Judy Golbuff and the others sparkled as they discussed the various programs. The girls had already immunized thousands of children in strange-sounding places such as Kotte and Dehiwala. There were more to come, and these young men who had hesitated at the thought of receiving their own immunizations were soon to learn how to be health workers and help save others from crippling or disabling disease.

Annette Hirsch, our health educator, recognized immediately one vital asset among these students. They were still young enough to identify and gain the confidence of the children with whom they were destined to work, and they were about the same age as many of the young teachers in the schools. She was determined to capitalize upon this. The group was soon augmented by the arrival of a younger but mature-for-her-years volunteer, Leslie Kron, a sixteen-year-old from Philadelphia and daughter of one of our volunteer surgeons. She, together with volunteer part-time help such as pretty Neall O'Melia, one of our young secretaries, was to provide the distaff side of the student program. The enthusiasm of the group as a whole was soon to involve almost everyone from the ship during their free time, a type of "infection" that had spread every summer before, even to our most senior physicians. Youth can be and still is pretty wonderful.

The briefing and concentrated training period for the students lasted only a few days and included visiting the various sites where they were to work. The leprosarium was early on the itinerary, and the entire group decided to finish the cleaning and painting of the wards begun earlier by Margaret Storkan. Each day one more ward was completed, and before long the entire leprosarium had a new look. The patients were delighted with their new volunteers and joined lustily in the guitar songfests put on by two of the students at the end of each day.

Next they decided to take on the Maradana School as a collective project, with individuals or pairs splitting off on certain days or evenings to carry out their other duties. John Walsh and Bill McDiarmid drew the assignment of physical education training at the jail. John, Bill, and Nick Secor undertook the assignment of teaching physical education and group games to the children at the school for the blind and the deaf. Bill, Jr., Leslie Kron, Steve Woodruff and all of the others, together with several public health and pediatric ward nurses (on their time off), concentrated on the Maradana School.

Watching these young people and the seriousness with which they carried out their assignments made us all proud. Each morning they would leave immediately after breakfast, carrying out individual assignments in the early hours, then converging on the Maradana School collectively for the remainder of the day. The principal of the school, H. R. Mendes, at first found it difficult to believe. No one had ever come forth to help him or his teachers in this fashion. This was new to Ceylon, and of anything that is not traditional in this culture one had to be cautious. But Mendes was captured completely by the enthusiasm of these students.

The school was filthy, classrooms in disrepair, and the courtyard in its center was littered with trash and old broken furniture. Personal hygiene was unknown and even the most fundamental and necessary habits were carried out on the spur of the moment and almost anywhere on the premises. The lack of money in the school budget prevented any health education, and the teachers themselves were dispirited. The most profound problem facing the American students was to combat the lethargy of faculty and students alike.

The school itself housed students from the lowest grades up through our equivalent of the tenth grade. It was a large, aged, two-story building in the center of a broken-down block. The street before it was not paved, and as you approached its gates it resembled an abandoned army barracks. The classrooms were laid out in a complete square around the littered courtyard, separated by walls from one another but without closed windows. The ventilation was more important than the windowpanes, but even with all of this air the odors in which the students had to work were nauseating. Yet they came to school. Truancy was no problem; illness and poverty definitely were. Those who were too sick remained at home; those big enough sometimes had to work if the work could be found.

The American students convinced Mendes that something could be done, and persuaded him to allow them to meet with his teachers to enlist their cooperation. Bill, Jr., outlined our ideas and made very clear that without the teachers' desire for improvement and willingness to join in, nothing could be accomplished. The school granted time to our health educators, nutritionists and other members of the public health team so that they could demonstrate and so teach the value of elementary hygiene, good habits and good nutrition. We had found that here in Ceylon, just as in many other countries, proper food was available but the poor had never been taught the importance of eating it. Just filling foods were consumed with no concern for nutrition. The teachers themselves joined in these classroom demonstrations as interpreters and at the same time learned the lessons themselves. Before we were finished, they were doing the teaching and doing it well.

Leslie and Neall, together with others, worked with the smaller girls, teaching them to play and to laugh together. The simple introduction of games to the classroom was an innova-

tion. The talent that some of the younger children had for sew-
ing and art encouraged the girls to empty the ship of the necessary implements to encourage these talents. Cloth and thread,
together with paints and paper came from everywhere.

The male students were encouraged to join in a massive
cleanup campaign which lasted for days. The Ceylonese youngsters even turned up to do volunteer work on Poya Days, something unheard of in modern Ceylon. Room after room was
scrubbed down and cleaned, some were painted. The schoolchildren developed a real pride in what they were accomplishing and felt that they wanted the best public school in all of
Colombo. Each night our cleanup crew returned to the ship exhausted and dirty but glowing with reports of the progress they
had made. The reward to us who watched them was that it was
not so much the visible improvement in the school but that feeling that they were reaching the teachers, the students and even
their families. The parents, curious about what their children
told them, had started to join in. Ceylonese medical students
and nursing students assigned to the ship wondered aloud why
they were not thoughtful enough themselves to have created this
spirit for change. The newspapers, many of whom had been so
critical of our efforts to introduce new methods, awakened to
what was happening and began to follow the progress at Maradana.

Then our student group began to wonder how the results
achieved could be retained when the summer was over. They
met and decided that the answer was going to be money for
continuing audiovisual aids, particularly in the field of health
education. The principal agreed with them. With regret, he told
them that no money would be forthcoming from the government, for what one school receives all must receive. This would
be impossible because of the sorry state of finances in Ceylon.
Not discouraged, they decided two things. The money required
should not be given to the school by *Hope* or by any charitable
donation from other sources, but be raised by the students and

parents. This was the time to find out if they had really succeeded in teaching the principles of self-help.

A meeting was called at the school and it was proposed by
our student chairman that there be a school fair. Certainly not
original for us at home, but a real stunner of an event to the
group at Maradana. Admission would be charged and exhibi-
tions be prepared by the students. The girls would sew aprons,
dish towels or anything their hearts desired, and the items
would be sold. Those children with talent would paint pictures
for an art exhibit and every picture painted would be for sale.
There would be demonstrations in the chemistry and physics
laboratory to prove to parents the value of education. Refreshments would be sold by volunteers among the parents (this in
the absence of anything resembling a PTA) and food of every
type would be for sale.

This all met with approval but also there arose the inevitable
problem—how could they possibly buy the materials needed or
the items to sell? No one had any money.

"We'll ask people to donate them," piped up one of the American students. "If we have to ask every merchant in Colombo,
we'll get what we need. But you will all have to help with the
asking too."

They were dubious, but once again Yankee enthusiasm was
too much for them to resist and they agreed. Beginning the next
day a horde of the *Hope* and the hoping descended on Colombo
—American students and Ceylonese teachers—parading from
door to door. They required a great deal. The initial response
was so encouraging that they decided to create a large game
room featuring virtually every game of chance usually seen at a
county fair—dart boards, ringtosses, roulette. But the most popular one turned out to be softball toss at a target which, if on
the mark, released an attached board. Seated on the end of this
board, suspended over a large tub of water, was to be H. R.
Mendes himself, the principal of the school. It promised to be a
long, wet day for him. But what better example of how far along

the road to voluntary participation this man had traveled in only a few short weeks?

Each evening all of the donations were brought back to the ship so that they could be stored for safekeeping. There was no place at the school in which anything could be locked away, and it seemed prudent to play it safe. The night before the fair, there were enough prizes for two full truckloads. The students at the school had worked all day cleaning and readying the building, and putting up their exhibits. They were fearful that something might be stolen, so our group packed the trucks with the prizes and drove to Maradana School, unloaded the treasures and spent the night sleeping in shifts at the school. It was a needless precaution, but the school authorities were so anxious for all to go well that it did not seem too much of a hardship.

The big day arrived, and I had been invited by Mr. Mendes to open the fair at ten A.M. When I reached Maradana School a large crowd had already gathered outside the closed gates. The press and photographers waited inside with the principal and his staff. Children in freshly washed clothes flanked him on either side. Across the entrance to the courtyard was a wide strip of ribbon and no one was to pass until I had exercised my privilege of cutting it. This was such a tribute to the American students that I insisted on Bill, Jr., and Mr. Mendes himself joining with me in a tripartite slice. I would not insult Mendes by refusing, nor could I accept the honor without sharing it with those who had made the day possible.

Formalities over with, the gates were open and the crowds came through as if they were going to the World Series. Everyone paid, and the principal beamed. The teachers and students were conscientious in their presentations and the parents were visibly impressed. The artwork disappeared like Picasso's, not the least of the buyers being *Hope* staffers and European embassy visitors. The game room resembled Las Vegas on New Year's Eve as lines of children tried their luck. Mr. Mendes was one wet principal after only an hour, so our students and even some of our nurses took turns at sitting on the ducking board. By the end of the day, more than two thousand rupees had been raised, a not inconsiderable sum in local currency. Its purchasing power on the local market was about the equivalent of the same amount in dollars at home. Mendes was overjoyed, and his students were the proudest in all Colombo. True to the spirit of their newfound democracy, the faculty was given the opportunity to vote on what the money should purchase. The decision was unanimous. The winner: new hygiene and health education teaching aids. A valuable lesson had been learned.

The principal was so pleased that he insisted on giving a dinner for the American students at his home, a compliment not offered lightly. The curries which he would proudly serve used up the total family protein budget for two weeks. He had grown very close to the students, and this was a grand gesture. The students, while grateful enough, were dubious over the prospect of the highly spiced curries with only a limited amount of water available as a chaser.

Seven of them made it to his house, and together with the six members of the Mendes clan filled his small living room. The principal promptly put them at ease with what he called his special, a cocktail made up of arrack mixed with champagne. Hors d'oeuvres were served and gave a hint of things to come. One of the boys downed seven bananas in very unsportsmanlike fashion, forcing his confreres to bear the brunt of the exotic spices. The dinner proved to be delightful, with Mrs. Mendes politely tempering her curry to suit the tastes of her American friends. Mendes regaled them with stories as he always did, some true and some perhaps somewhat exaggerated. His tales of hunting and fishing in Ceylon portrayed every animal or fish as the largest ever seen or caught.

When he began to tell about the python he had captured alive and brought home as a pet, they felt he was pulling their collective leg. He regaled them with the advantages a python has over a dog as a house pet—much cleaner, eats only once every two

and a half months, doesn't bark, certainly a better protector of
his house once people know he's there. Politely, skeptically and
with an abundance of arrak warming his innards, one of the
more astute students asked to see his Ceylonese Rin-Tin-Tin.
Mendes asked his oldest boy, age seven, to fetch the little dar-
ling from his box in the other room. He was somewhat apolo-
getic, for he was concerned about the snake's possible misbe-
havior. He hadn't eaten for three months and was overdue.
The boys were now certain it was a gag and settled back, relaxed but waiting. Young Mendes then reentered the room with
an eight-foot python draped around his neck. The boys froze,
their eyes popping. Seven glasses were promptly drained as one.

Mendes took the snake with loving care from his son and
began fondling it as if it were a dog. Not wishing to be discour-
teous, he walked toward the couch where three of *Hope*'s brav-
est were sitting. Calmly, he explained that his reptile was the
friendliest in Ceylon. He did add that it might be best if no one
made any sudden movements. He assured them that the flicker-
ing movements of his pet's tongue were not a demonstration of
either desire or anger, but the snake's way of "hearing." He extended his arms and placed the snake on the laps of the students. Any thought of being labeled as ugly Americans by refusing to hold the snake was now replaced by abject cowardice.
The python was passed around rapidly; the strong, cold body of
the snake slithered around the boys' necks, arms and legs much
like an inquiring dog or cat. Pet indeed!

The evening ended soon after, and as they were riding home
one of the boys expressed the thought that maybe they had over-
stayed their welcome. Another answered, still shaken, "Well, it's
one way to get your guests to go home."

The next day the student group was to experience the beginning of a tragedy which touched every one of us. Leslie Kron,
who had worked so tirelessly with them all through the month,
had complained of nausea and a headache. She was put to bed

and, when her condition worsened, was hospitalized in our intensive care unit that same afternoon. Her fever climbed precipitously despite all efforts to help her. The medical skill of the entire *Hope* community turned to in one of the most dramatic efforts to save a life that I have ever seen. Leslie was one of our own; her father had served *Hope* as a volunteer surgeon four different times. This year he had brought his wife and children to Ceylon with him so they could feel the same gratification that he himself had experienced each time he worked with the Project. Ironically the life we tried hardest to save and failed was that of his daughter. She was suffering from an overwhelming staphylococcal infection which invaded her bloodstream and resisted all drugs. For twenty-seven hours she, and everyone on board, fought for her life. The greater part of this period she was in merciful coma. Her death cast a pall of depression over the ship, as well as a reminder of how much there was yet to learn in overcoming disease.

It was Sam and Jean Kron who, with their courage, buoyed our spirits instead of our bringing comfort to them. Despite the rapidity and shock of the loss of this wonderful child, they helped us to live with our failure. They knew we had tried, and that the care she had received was the best we had to offer. But the life that was lost could not be brought back, and we felt very bitter with our sorrow. Why should a child like this, who was giving of herself for the good of others, be taken away, while so many others bent only on destruction are spared? It was not exactly a Christian thought, for no one's life should unnecessarily be taken; but it did cross my mind. The only consolation which I could give myself was the belief in what I told others who had suffered loss. The Lord must have wanted Leslie very much, else he would have let her stay with us, and with *Hope*.

CHAPTER 15

As is frequently the case, the aftermath of disaster is a rebirth of spirit. The death of Leslie Kron united the staff into working in a way which it had not been before. Many programs and individuals had been highly successful, and close and sincere friendships had developed between many of the Ceylonese physicians and their American colleagues. But we realized that our own internal communication had been sadly deficient. The interdependence of so many services in the hospital that were so evident during Leslie's battle for life were revealed in their excellence and in their importance to one another. So many had been involved in solving their own problems, they had neglected to find how others were accomplishing their ends.

This lack of communication internally had been a new experience for *Hope*. Some felt that this, the largest program *Hope* had ever attempted, was too large. It had required the dispatch of a portion of our staff to Kandy and others had to live ashore in Colombo because of insufficient accommodations on board. Others were overwhelmed by the vituperativeness of the communist press instead of ignoring it. They felt unappreciated and in some instances unwanted—exactly what the communists were endeavoring to make them believe. There were those who had been baffled by the indirectness of the Ceylonese personality and who had grown tired of trying to find a solution. The reasons were varied, and each was convinced that his or her singular disappointment was the greatest.

I was determined to find a way to draw *Hope* together and, in the intimacy and despair which followed our family tragedy, most of the staff was available for discussion, remaining close to the ship outside of working hours. It was our rotators, the volunteer physicians, who concerned me the most. The paramedical and nursing programs had been going well. Kandy was on solid ground and the morale of their group, including the assigned physician volunteers, was good.

Late one afternoon, I scheduled a session with a group of rotators in the "jungle." This is the name given to the quarters where some of the most renowned men in American medicine live during their tenure on board. It is a former hospital ward for staff, now converted into living quarters for our volunteers. Twenty-two men lived in this one room, in double-tiered bunks. They each had only a small locker for their clothes, and shared two showers, a small snack kitchen and a miniscule sitting room area. There was one desk for all to share, and if anyone wanted to read at night he had to lie down in his bunk in order to do it. The one advantage was its proximity to one of the boat deck laundry rooms. This enabled them to keep their wash-and-wear clean. The more helpless, or should I say clever, were able to prevail upon the nurses on permanent staff to mother them sufficiently to keep them in clean linen. They used to lie in wait until they heard one of the girls on the other side of the door, and then would step out and plaintively ask "How do you work those machines?" What could a girl do except come to their rescue?

Few ever complained about the jungle; in fact most of them preferred it. If on occasion there was a man unable to adapt to the environs of the area, we would find another place for him. Even so, one would find more often than not he was back in the jungle every night so as not to miss the bull sessions. This was where I chose to speak informally with them; this was where they let their hair down.

They were tired; they had been working hard. It was heartening to find that only a few were discouraged, and these worked in the specialties that we knew were trouble spots. I was surprised to find that these men had not been forewarned when they came on board. The explanation given to me later was logical but, unhappily, wrong. It was felt that it was a mistake to precondition newcomers to an adverse reaction; hence, the gamble that they would progress on their own initiative. It was a gamble that had failed. As they talked, it became evident that those who had been having considerable success were reluctant to speak of it to their colleagues who were so depressed. Internal communications had broken down. Many of the physicians were unaware of the success of the paramedical programs and had forgotten the vital role they themselves perform in the success of these efforts. They became excited as I told them of the success at Kandy, of the satisfaction in the nursing program. Then some of their own colleagues told them of their own successes, and the lift to this small but unhappy group was immediately visible.

They suggested more frequent staff meetings so that the entire group could share in the successes of the others, especially those who were living at the hotel (at three dollars a day) and who had coalesced into their own group. I was chagrined also to discover that there had been no representative from Kandy reporting to the staff with any consistency, so that Kandy's real advances with the students, the curriculum and the people were unknown to most of our ship's staff. Unfortunately meetings had purposely been lessened in number by those in charge because they felt the teaching schedule was so heavy that our staff would object to them. It was a judgment and decision sincerely made, but unfortunately it had proven to be incorrect. Lack of communication, the disease of our times, had struck the *Hope*. But it was to be a problem no longer!

We acted upon the suggestions of the rotators, and morale improved visibly within a matter of days. Walt Rogers started cracking the whip and redefined the functions of our coordinators. With increased responsibility and authority, each of our major services tightened up. Decisions were made to expand our activities rather than diminish them. New ideas were accepted and tried as people started talking. Our physicians and technicians were assigned to hospitals other than the massive Colombo General Complex.

Bob Kradjian moved his surgical volunteers into Colombo South, where the staff had been begging for our participation for weeks. Delayed by bureaucracy, the decision was made to respond to the invitation on our own and hope that the Health Ministry would live with it. Politics being what they are, the Health Minister was delighted but could not, for internal reasons, have issued the invitation through official channels. He had told us on our arrival that we were free to go anywhere that we were invited, but bureaucrats on a lower level had made veiled warnings to the contrary. Unfortunately, they were listened to.

One such invitation from a hospital in Ceylon read as follows. I dare not quote a name or place, for in this wonderful land socialized medicine reigns supreme. If a man is too critical of the sytem, he can be summarily sent to the boondocks and even assigned in a field in which he has no skills. The letter was addressed to me and read as follows.

This is a personal letter to you, and NOT an official one. If I were to write officially to you, it would have to be channelled through several administrators (Medical Superintendant of my hospital, then the Superintendant of Health Service of my division, through the Director of Health Services for the island, and finally through the Ministry of Health for our country). At any one of these levels, the official letter could be delayed or stayed, if the officials felt they did not see eye to eye with me, or felt inclined to disagree with me, or felt that my letter amounted to adverse criticism of their work. Hence, as this is a private personal letter to you, please do not hand it over to our Governmental Officials, but please be free to draw your own conclusions and act on them, from my observations, comments, suggestions, etc., so that the wonderful "Hope" project could be more effective in Ceylon.

The letter went on to describe the difficulties in obtaining an assignment to the *Hope* because the British-trained hierarchy did not want others to be exposed to American techniques. This was the case despite the fact that the *Hope* was in Ceylon in response to an invitation fully concurred in by their medical profession and its hierarchy. The opposition clique was small, but had friends in powerful places—always a danger where there is bureaucracy.

It was into these previously shut-off areas that we now boldly moved. The Minister himself chuckled, for by our initiative we had solved his problems. Since he had not formally passed the invitation through official channels, the clique could not condemn him. If he were to stop us, it would be politically bad locally among the other physicians and an act of discourtesy totally foreign to the Ceylonese. They could be aggravating at times, but were always kind, gentle and infinitely courteous.

Invitations from the medical communities at Jaffna, Ratnapura, Batticoloa, and Galle were accepted, and medical-nursing-teaching teams of eight to ten people were welcomed. One of our surgeons had an interesting experience in Jaffna, which he recounted with great delight. Upon the team's arrival at the hospital, the entire staff was present. Our group had no idea of what to expect but thought they were prepared for anything. The first request was a beaut!

"Please tell us, Doctor, with all candor, what do you think is wrong with the way we practice medicine in Ceylon." Our surgeon and team leader was somewhat taken aback, having been thoroughly briefed on the fact that the Ceylonese avoid direct methods of confrontation. Recovering quickly, he decided that this was the chance that we had all been waiting for and resolved to be just as candid as the questioner.

"All right," he answered, "I will. Let us accept the fact that a significant number of your specialists are well trained. They have been trained in England and worship all that is British, even if the technique they are practicing was discarded twenty years ago. They worship the letters and multiple degrees after one another's name, rather than the medical ability to perform. As you know, under the old British system you could be qualified in surgery at a variety of different schools, all on the basis of the same training but different examinations. The result is that the degrees mean little except for the first one earned.

"The operating room habits that we have observed in the general hospital are poor. Sterile technique is abandoned by some under the excuse they are overworked. Your men are busy, but not that busy. Your socialized system prevents them from doing as much as they could, therefore there is no reason for haste. You will not accept nurse anesthetists, and yet your anesthesiologists must leave the room when a patient is anesthetized in order to prepare the next patient. You know that is bad technique, and dangerous to the patient. But you have permitted the system to make you apathetic. The fundamental precautions necessary for good anesthesia are not carried out. Why bother to use a blood pressure cuff and stethoscope if the anesthesiologist is not in the room?" He went on and on for almost fifteen minutes, pouring forth all the frustrations and repressed criticism that he and others had been holding back for weeks. He spoke of the reluctance of the Ceylonese to learn new techniques simply because they were taught by Americans.

There was not a sound in the room each time our spokesman

paused. His voice was soft and even, not angry. What had to be said, he was saying. He feared he was treading upon dangerous ground, but given the opportunity he could do no less.

When he had finished, his questioner smiled and said, "Thank you, Doctor, for your honesty. This is the result of government medicine. However, here we are outside of the political mainstream, and you will find things somewhat different. Perhaps, you might even find them worse than in Colombo. We shall give you the chance to show us how you do things in America. Tomorrow, you will operate in our hospital."

It was difficult to tell whether he had his tongue in cheek or not, but he was serious about the surgery. As soon as the meeting broke up, our surgeon was led to a clean hospital ward and was shown a case lying in bed, a man about thirty, scheduled for surgery the next morning. The case was discussed, and a removal of a major portion of the patient's stomach was planned. Our man agreed after hearing the history, examining the patient and reviewing the X rays. Once again he was a young resident who was to be tested. He wondered whether the local staff had a surprise in store for him. They seemed friendly, and following the examination of the patient their chief of staff took our entire team out to dinner. It was a pleasant evening, and not another word was said about the practice of medicine.

The next morning our doctor arrived at the hospital and proceeded to the surgical dressing room. It was immaculate. Scrub suits were plentiful and his Ceylonese colleagues followed perfect preoperative technique. When he entered the operating rooms, the X rays were displayed on a view box, the anesthesiologist was in his assigned place. The patient was properly draped, a blood pressure cuff was on his arm and everything appeared as if he were in the university hospital at home. Many of the physicians had come into the room to observe the surgery, all properly capped, masked and gowned—an absolute first for us to see in Ceylon.

The operation itself was almost anticlimactic. All went well, and as our man explained his technique, which was different from the one the local surgeons had been using, the operating theater became alive with questions, comments and vital exchanges of information. This was what we had come for! Not to humiliate, denigrate or pontificate, but to teach and exchange ideas. Here in this dusty, hot city of Jaffna we found an eagerness to learn as well as a desire to teach us what they knew.

After the conclusion of the surgery, our successful but somewhat abashed professor apologized to his Ceylonese colleagues for generalizing in his impressions of medicine in Ceylon. Somewhat sheepishly, he thanked them for teaching him this lesson. They in turn were proud and pleased. They had made their point. Colombo was not Ceylon, and please come back to Jaffna. Believe me, we did; many, many times. We had both moved one step closer to understanding one another.

Similar experiences occurred in the other cities outside of Colombo. Many of our friends at the Colombo General Complex tried to explain the difference, but no matter how kindly it was expressed, their own intellectual arrogance came through. The physicians in the other cities were reputed simply to be not as competent, and therefore could learn a great deal from us. The most qualified were assigned by the government to Colombo, at least in the opinion of the Ceylonese. It was true that assignment to Colombo was in recognition of a man's presumed excellence. Unfortunately it was also a direct reflection of his political connections. If a physician was both competent and well connected, the people would benefit. It was our experience to find that many of the physicians in the so-called "outstations" were not only of equal or greater skill than those in the metropolis but were also possessed of that optimum requirement of any physician, humility.

There were many aspects of the political system of medicine which were now brought before our staff that had not been understood before. For example, sometimes men trained in one specialty were transferred to an outstation with an assignment to practice another. This was very demoralizing. In a nation with almost insurmountable health problems there were many physicians who were "unemployed" and unable to practice in government hospitals. The investment made in their education was wasted because of supposed deficiencies of funds. The previous government had been communist oriented and had sent sixty students to the Soviet Union to study medicine. They were about to finish their training, but there was no intention to give them licensure when they returned. The reasons were not political in this instance, but a refusal of the medical faculties to recognize anything but British medical training. This was not to protect the standards of health care for the people, but to protect the sinecure of the men at the top in Colombo. The Russians did not have to feel slighted, for American training was not officially recognized either.

Each of our own visiting physician volunteers, many of whom were department chairmen in medical schools at home, had to receive special permission to perform their functions as physicians in Ceylon even to teach. This is a normal procedure for any country, but in Ceylon, had they wished to remain, their previous education would not have been recognized and they would have had to go to medical school again even to become eligible to take the examination. This is the extent to which nationalism can go, and explains in part why it is so difficult to carry out successful foreign aid programs.

As a result of these meetings and discussions, we reorganized our department of education on board and charged Doctor "Pete" Morrow with its responsibility. Pete was a taciturn, quiet New England type from the University of Vermont Medical School. Stubborn and experienced, in his own way he accomplished a great deal. He spent hours of his time ferreting out the individual problems faced by various physicians in their relationships to their counterparts. He encouraged more social and off-the-record contact, which paid off admirably in improving relationships between the medical school at the University in

Colombo and ourselves. Above all, he listened to Tom Bowles
and his suggestion that the Ceylonese medical students from
Kandy be accepted on the *Hope* for short periods of exposure to
American teaching methods.

Prior to this time, it had been the feeling on board that students had to spend a longer period of time than just a few
weeks in order to profit from the experience. Tom had discussed
the problem with Dean Bibile at Kandy and explained that
"under the Ceylonese system a student may choose the professors under whom he wishes to study. This sometimes results in a
vast disproportion of students assigned to one man or the other.
A professor may be chosen because he marks easily, is amusing
in class, or it is traditionally required that a student serve with
him because of the reverence with which he is held in the country.

"Our own students at home should see the fallacy and weakness of this kind of system, and perhaps they would move more
slowly.

"Once that professor is chosen, there is no opportunity to
change and his examination is the only one on which the student is graded. Therefore, if some students absent themselves
from class to go to the ship, they may be failed. Bibs had succeeded in persuading some of the professors to release their students from the school in Kandy for short periods on the condition that they were permitted and required to report honestly in
writing their views of the quality of education they received."

Pete felt this approach was a good idea, particularly in view
of the new curriculum being planned for the school at Kandy
with the help of our teaching unit. It was evident that if the
thirty-one house officers already training with us on board were
supplemented by students, our own physicians would be very
stimulated. The house officers themselves could be taught to
participate more fully in teaching, and the students would have
an exposure to something outside of their own environment.
However short the tour, whether it be two weeks or six, the

*Hope* was a piece of the United States and the visit would be beneficial to us all.

Much depended upon the reaction of the first group, for it was they who would tell their colleagues and their faculty of their experience. This was the story of *Hope* in Ceylon, always being tested, always being probed. It is understandable, no matter how aggravating, for we have no right to expect that simply because we are Americans everything that we preach must be accepted as gospel. The program was instituted and became an immediate success. The enthusiasm of these young men and women was an inspiration. Fully half of the medical students in Ceylon are women, and to watch these sari-clad, dainty but determined young things in the wards would have stimulated anyone. Our staff felt that they had to give the best that was in them.

The students from Perideniya (Kandy) were the guinea pigs, but the experiment was so successful that soon we had "competing" groups from the school in Colombo. We stressed thoroughness in history taking and examinations, responsibility to the patient as his or her case, record keeping, differential diagnosis, interdisciplinary cooperation and the use of auxiliary medical help. This was done through the technique of bedside teaching and multiple small conferences. It may seem fundamental, but the departure from the stress on didactic or lecture-form teaching and respect for other members of the medical team were very new. The encouragement of the students' participation and suggestions on each case probably impressed them more than anything. Pete, who had received less than unanimous support for this experiment, was delighted at its result. The only one happier was Tom Bowles, who had persuaded Bibs to agree to the experiment.

A few quotations from the reports of the students themselves say it best.

"During discussions, the student is encouraged to make his own contribution and criticism of the case. If the group is convinced that the students' suggestions are reasonable, they are implemented and the student is complimented."

"In Ceylon," said another, "the students' suggestions and criticisms regarding the cases are not accepted with the same readiness and hence the student is hesitant to make any contributions even if he is keen on doing so."

"The surgeon takes a more active part in the post-operative care of the patient," wrote a third. "They work as a team—surgeons, house officers and nurses. Any special problems relating to a particular system are advised on by the specialist in that particular field. Any useful suggestions by students are accepted and carried out, too."

"We observed that improved nutrition and efficient nursing, using aseptic techniques, are beneficial to the patient," said another.

Finally, another stated: "We were also impressed by the kindness shown to patients by the hospital personnel and by the coordinated teamwork that existed among medical personnel like the physician, surgeon, pathologist, radiologist, etc."

From the sentiments of these five reports came the capsule of all that we wanted to teach in Ceylon. Thank God for the young who understood and gave a new momentum to our efforts. We were not attempting to train already trained surgeons, but only to remind them that to operate alone without remembering all of the other lessons was not enough. More, we wanted to remind them of their obligation to teach the young so that the future of medicine in Ceylon would be assured. The day of the prima donna in medicine is gone. So much of his success depends on many others. The young realized immediately that to gain respect you must first give it. To improve the caliber of your auxiliary personnel, you had to appreciate their efforts. These five young students had seen in two weeks more than many of their seniors had seen in months. The road ahead was bright.

# CHAPTER 16

"Here at whatever hour you come you will find light and help and human kindness." These are the words printed above the entrance to the Lady Ridgeway Hospital, the principal children's hospital in Ceylon. This is the motto which the pediatricians in this overcrowded hospital tried to make a reality. Lady Ridgeway is a six-hundred-bed hospital that rarely housed less than nine hundred patients. As was the case in Kandy, there were frequently two to a bed, and often some children slept upon mats on the floor. The medical staff desperately tried to keep ahead of the situation but it was impossible; there were simply too many sick children. Another common problem was locating the parents once a patient had been cured and was ready to go home.

The outpatient clinic was a massive room which began filling with children and their parents early each morning. By nine it was like Times Square on New Year's Eve. More than two thousand patients queued up for dressings, treatments, injections or just to be screened. Some were old enough to stand, others had to be held by parents who looked so frail themselves one wondered if they would survive the day. What appeared to be an uncontrolled mob was actually tightly packed lines of patients, orderly in their own fashion.

As they stood in line some mothers nursed their babies, others diapered theirs. Some children stood in their place naked, for not every family could afford clothes for all of the small children. None tried to push forward, no matter how sick their youngster may have been. They patiently waited their turn. None left the line for any reason. The result was that pools of urine and deposits of excreta collected on the floor as the day went on. There was no solution; this was the system.

At the end of each day the smell of the clinic was quite indescribable. But the floors would be quickly washed, whatever lavatories that may have been used were cleansed with disinfectant, and the breeze filtered through the empty clinics to carry away the odors in time for the same events to begin again the next morning. The physicians were utterly defeated by the circumstances. I spoke with one of them early in the year and offered to make an effort to obtain funds for remodeling the clinic area so that an equal or even greater number of patients could be handled in a more orderly and certainly a more sanitary fashion. He was extremely grateful, but urged me not to say any more about it. When I appeared puzzled, he shook his head sadly and said, "I know that your intentions are good. Unfortunately, if you did find the necessary money" (at local labor rates it would have required less than ten thousand dollars) "you would not be able to give it to us. You would have to give it to the government. They would find some reason to not give the funds to this hospital, but you would never know it. Then we would be criticized by the government for giving the impression that we had complained to you about our deficiencies. Someone would be transferred as punishment, so little would be accomplished. You know, there are none so proud as the poor. A poor nation sometimes is proud to the point of stupidity. And then, too, we have learned to live with these problems."

I smiled in understanding because I knew he spoke the truth. This was one of the kindest and most compassionate physicians I had met in Ceylon. I had watched him with his patients and with his students and knew how much he wanted better facilities than those with which he was working. Yet he was already resigned to a life of disappointment and had the same ability to bear it as so many other Ceylonese.

Given the handicaps under which the physicians of Lady Ridgeway labored, one realized they practiced good medicine. Still children frequently died of dehydration when intravenous fluids were not available. There were periodic shortages of all drugs and equipment. At such times the pediatrician could only be kind and hope for the best. They endeavored to separate their infectious cases from the other children, but it was often impossible. If chicken pox broke out on a ward, it would sweep through the entire hospital. Deaths from complicating pneumonias were not unusual. Measles was a critical disease in Ceylon, and there was no vaccine to combat it. Hepatitis was common. Rheumatic fever and advanced rheumatic heart disease were more widespread than I have ever seen anywhere. The severity of the cardiac disease in children was remarkable. The government had only recently invested in the training of an open-heart surgical team in an effort to help these children. Unfortunately, it was far more of a prestige development than it was a practical one. Prevention is so much cheaper and safer.

The wards in the hospital were all open, and the walls of some were painted. Each physician had his own ward and there was some cooperation between them. Once again the system intervened and each man had to fight for his own supplies and his patients' welfare. It was not unusual to find dogs or cats wandering through the wards looking for scraps of food. In one way, this was a blessing, for the children had no toys and those that could played with the animals. Heaven knows how much this contributed to cross-infection, but no one seemed disturbed. The ever-present and brazen crows, protected from destruction by religious beliefs and as large as small dogs, also flew through the wards picking up anything edible or shiny.

If youngsters had to be taken to special clinics for any reason, the shortage of attendants and wheelchairs made it necessary to gather them up much like a litter of puppies. Babies lay on rubber sheets, hot and wet, for there was not enough help to change linen. Nor, in fact, was there enough linen. Patient identification was always haphazard, for patients were not tagged and their identification was casual. How it was possible to give proper and appropriate medication is still a mystery to me.

The nurses worked in the midst of this confusion, and the pediatricians and their students made rounds. The basic necessities for care to the more seriously ill were present. The hospital diet consisted primarily of bread, rice and a little milk. Parents were free to supplement the diet if they were able, but few were. Despite all of these handicaps, the doctors were imperturbable and worked hard, and accomplished some amazing results. The only real complaints I ever heard were over what was considered inadequate laboratory work.

There was only one operating theater in the hospital, and it was well below standard. In an effort to make the government do something to support the Ceylonese surgeons' complaints, we even found tetanus bacteria in a culture of sweepings from the operating room floor. Though the government laboratory confirmed our findings, nothing was done. A badly needed addition to the hospital with five operating theaters in its plans had been under construction for years. Money kept running out, governments changed and the work was intermittently discontinued. This incompleted wing was used as a further excuse for not spending further funds to repair already existing facilities.

After many years of working in countries with financial difficulties, we in HOPE certainly have grown to understand the problems of poverty. However, we will never learn to understand indifference. Caste, unions and the time off for vacation and sick leave—as required under a socialized system—could prevent many nations from ever getting on their feet. Add the observation of weeks of compulsory religious holidays, and a worker is off as frequently as he is on. The caste system prevents certain levels of employees from doing lower-level work, thus increasing costs and lowering efficiency. It has even been reasoned that it is more economical to keep some children in the hospital for a year and feed them, than it is to train or employ additional physicians. This is economics, Asian style. The Western community will never learn to comprehend it fully.

But of all of the professional contacts made by the *Hope* staff, none were more pleasant or rewarding than those at Lady Ridgeway. True, there were problems with the pediatricians but not of the petty kind we had become accustomed to at Colombo General. Each doctor here was so anxious to have our consultant work with them that the prime difficulty was how to divide our pediatricians six ways. It was finally decided that each *Hope* physician would serve one week with each Ceylonese pediatrician and his students on his ward, but be available for consultation at all times for each of the others. Since there were six wards assigned and our pediatricians would be available only two months because of our rotation system, obviously someone would have to get the short end of the exchange.

Each Friday there would be a general conference, with each of the local pediatricians presenting an interesting case for discussion. This satisfied everyone. The system was not perfect, but it was the basis of the finest teaching and exchange program of the year. Additional American pediatricians directed their attention to the premature and newborn nurseries at the two maternity hospitals, both of which were being reorganized as far as nursing goes by *Hope* staff nurses. Fortunately, the same Ceylonese pediatricians were consultants to these centers. They were very amenable to suggestions and marked improvement resulted, particularly in the most fundamental areas. It's difficult to believe that in the twentieth century nurses had to be taught to pick up babies in order to feed them in a premature nursery; or that body temperature must be checked frequently to prevent an infant from dying of shock resulting from marked hypothermia; or that individual towels can be resterilized and reused as needed, instead of using one towel a day on all of the babies in the nursery, exposing the well ones to infection from the sick ones. The Ceylonese physicians knew better but could not cross the caste barrier and interfere with nursing practice. Our nurse, Nancy Fern, had to bring these changes about at a nurse-to-nurse level. There were many other areas of improvement in coordination between the delivery suite area and the premature nursery, such as those preventing death from asphyxiation as a result of poor aspiration technique or a lack of suction apparatus. But thank heaven these changes were made. At least the living had a better chance to live.

What we were seeing was actually a situation where first-rate pediatricians were forced to practice third-rate pediatrics. If local pride had not been so great, we could have done a better job ourselves; our wards on the ship were well staffed and well equipped. But in our endeavor not to teach procedures that could not be carried on after we departed, we ourselves lowered our standards to a degree. For instance, we did not provide in our laboratory the more sophisticated tests that the Ceylonese wanted us to demonstrate to their students. Some of us still feel this was correct. Why add to their frustration? Others felt we should have demonstrated them and perhaps embarrassed the government into providing needed equipment and material for the local hospitals. I am still inclined to lean toward stressing the necessity of demonstrating fundamentally good medicine in the way it will have to be practiced after we leave a country. It is not nearly so important to satisfy the small number, in need of exotic procedures, at the expense of the majority. I wish that some of our major medical centers here in the United States would follow the same examples, and worry more about people than prestige.

With all of the heartache that accompanies sickness in children, their spontaneity and liveliness as they get well always adds a spark. The pediatric wards on the *Hope* were always cluttered with volunteers who wanted to take the children out on deck or go into the play area and amuse the youngsters by teaching them games. Off-duty nurses and students were forever taking groups of convalescents to some corner where they played the guitar and sang to what was doubtlessly the most appreciative audience in the world.

The small boys in particular loved the students very much. In Ceylon the children are brought up almost completely by the mother until they are well into their teens. This affects the male personality considerably. A Ceylonese boy becomes gentle and passive and develops none of the competitive spirit we are accustomed to in our own young boys. This is seen particularly in their approach to athletics: winning or losing means little or nothing. Dr. Tom Bowles was asked to coach the basketball team at the University in Perideniya, and almost drove himself mad trying to make the boys competitive under the basket. It never took.

Each year in Ceylon there is a basketball tournament sponsored by one of the colleges, St. Benedict's, which traditionally wins. This team represented Ceylon in both the Asian games and the Olympic games. Our summer students were invited to pull a team together and enter the tournament. None of our lads had ever played basketball, although two of them had played football, one lacrosse, one hockey and two others soccer and tennis. But all had played competitively in school. The team they were to play against had been practicing for weeks and was drawn from the army, the police and other groups. Our lads worked all day, were busy almost every evening and never had much opportunity to practice. But they reached the finals of the tournament, going through twelve games without a defeat and with embarrassingly one-sided scores. Fortunately, St. Benedict's beat them in the finals by simply running them into the ground, thereby avoiding a very ticklish situation. The success of our boys was due only to the competitive spirit they had grown up with, not their skill. Some of the local players were accomplished athletes in excellent condition physically, but they could not shake the gentility and passiveness that was ingrained in them.

This experience made it easier to understand why women will eventually dominate the professions in Ceylon, and why they are already a very significant political force. The phenomenon is common not only to Ceylon but to other nations in this area, such as India, Indonesia, and Vietnam, a part of the tradition in child rearing which will not change and is as much a part of the culture as its religious base.

Competitive or not, a child's enthusiasm is without limit. One evening Mary Lou Panter, one of our pediatric nurses, discovered that one of her children had come into the ward bearing a "beastie" in his head. It was a garden variety "louse." Fearing the worst had already happened, Mary Lou armed herself with a flashlight and a magnifying glass and made an inspection tour of the sleeping heads in the ward. Each inspection awakened a child, and unfortunately one after the other was seen to be already hosting one or more inhabitants like that on the head in the first crib. Several new admissions had come in that afternoon and had obviously brought the lice with them. Each time a youngster was discovered to be infected, he thought it was part of a game and jumped out of bed to follow the nurse and her flashlight around. Before she was finished, Pied Piper Mary Lou had ten youngsters following her around, all giggling at the show. Only two passed muster, and these clean cherubs felt distinctly left out.

Mary Lou envisioned all twenty-five children on board infected by the next morning, so she lined up the louse bearers, and in assembly-line fashion shaved their locks and gave each a medicated shampoo. There wasn't much sleep in the ward that night, but the laughter could be heard all over the ship.

Laughter is always the best medicine for children, and the *Hope* tradition of giving each child a toy he could call his own was carried on in Ceylon. Many of these youngsters had never owned a toy and found it difficult to believe that at last they had one of their own. They held on to them as if their very lives depended on it. The gratitude and love that filled their eyes cannot be put into words. But how can there be enough toys manufactured for children in a country where the crippled have to wait as much as two years for the manufacture of one set of braces?

We can all still remember the youngster who literally crawled aboard the S.S. *Hope* one day in an almost apelike manner. His arms swung outward and his legs were bowed. Several years earlier he had suffered an attack of transverse myelitis, an infection of the spinal cord. He was partially paralyzed from the waist down. His lower limbs were weak and without sensation. He loped rather than walked, and only for about ten feet, and then fell. He could not be cured, but we knew that with braces and crutches he would do much better. The Ceylonese physicians also knew this, but there was the two-year waiting period for the braces from the only brace shop on the entire island. The volume of patients requiring help is staggering, and under the system of political medicine one waits his turn.

In this instance, no permanent deformity appeared to have occurred, so our prosthetist and physical therapist went right to work. Within four days the boy was walking upright with a new sense of dignity thanks to his braces and crutches. Hopefully as he grows the Ceylonese charged with his care will continue to provide adjustments for him. None could deny the glow and glory in his face.

Being a pediatrician anywhere is both rewarding and heartrending. On the *Hope*, it is the extreme of both. Doctor Barry Panter, the coordinator of our pediatric service on board and husband of Mary Lou, was no exception. He was a terribly sensitive man and experienced emotional exhaustion daily. One evening he wrote a poem about his patients which tells it all. It was called "The Hidden Children."

A child comes to our ship. His ribs like the rungs of a ladder
   climb up his frail chest. He stands, quiet and forlorn.
   His sunken eyes have no interest in this world.
This is malnutrition.
And always present is a heartbreaking apathy.
   Placed in bed, he sits unmoving. Without a smile, and without a tear.
   A child who has learned that nothing, and no one, comes from crying.
Somewhere, behind that wall, a child is hidden.
   With love, with food, and with time—glimpses of him may be seen.
   Cecil holds fiercely to a yellow balloon.
   And Justin cries if another child has his checkered hat.
   Mallika gently rubs her face against a fuzzy animal.
And then more openly—a hesitant, questioning smile—
   a small hand placed in yours—a child climbing into your lap to be held.
Come out Cecil. Come out Mallika and Justin.
Come out. Come out, wherever you are. Please come out."

# CHAPTER 17

It was Shakespeare who wrote "The hardest knife ill-used doth lose his edge." Each year aboard the *Hope* some of us are tempted to forget this, most frequently because we are what we are, Americans. As a people we are dedicated to getting the job done, and are not blessed with an overabundance of patience. Proud of our flexibility, we sometimes find it difficult to disguise irritability. By early summer, some of our staff had reached this point. We had become weary of being caught in the middle between the physicians facing an impossible task and a government doing its best to make work a political system so foreign to our own. No one was at fault, but the time had come either to move ahead or move out.

We had developed a deep affection for the people, and an excellent rapport with the vast majority of physicians. But the small core of die-hard opposition had become more stubborn. We simply could not understand why the greater number did not overwhelm the others. The reason was that we could not still fully comprehend the degree of professional pride involved. A few of the specialists refused even to speak with us. One of their patriarchal members stoutly observed one day that "Many come to Ceylon to teach, only to find that they have come to learn." It was a pontifical observation, and one in which he sincerely believed. He could not accept the premise that we were indeed willing to learn as well as teach. However, in order to accomplish this end a dialogue had to be established. Unbelievable as it may sound, he and his small coterie of colleagues believed that somehow their own government had conspired to embarrass them.

If any public attention was given to a success by a *Hope* staff member, it was taken by some as a personal reflection upon the ability of the local profession. We had not come to perform miracles, nor had we ever implied that we could. Some of the public expected them nevertheless, and the local physicians did not help this situation by attempting to refer to us every incurable in Ceylon. It was depressing to have to say day after day to patients who had waited weeks for appointments, "*bohoma kanagatoo*" (very sorry), and to watch the tears fill their eyes as their last hope was dashed. On other occasions when we were able to help, some resented our success.

We had tried praising this small, resentful group. Our own senior medical officer told all who would listen of the respect we held for the skill of local physicians, but they accepted this without in return recognizing the skills of our teachers. And so we persuaded our own impatient staff to continue working as well as they could, certain that their quality would ultimately be appreciated. I personally—and with some vehemence—advised those who continued to trouble us from the Colombo side that we intended to fulfill our mission despite them. It was now our policy to move softly, neither praise nor condemn anyone, and let the local opposition come to us.

The Health Minister understood our difficulty. Passive cooperation with us was the only course left open to him by that small group who wished to cause him and the incumbent government political discomfort. The nursing and paramedical programs continued to be highly successful, and the medical students and house officers became our strongest allies. It was dif-

ficult to turn the other cheek, but the wisdom of the decision
began to demonstrate itself in a matter of days. It takes two
sides to create a conflict, and as long as we were able to resist
the temptation to participate in one, the opposition soon began
to lose its steam. We had learned and accepted that we could not
revolutionize the approach to the practice of medicine in Ceylon. On the other hand, they had learned that we were a stubborn and confident group who could not easily be discouraged.

It was to be a long, hot summer but one which was marked
by a drastic turn upward for our program. The *Hope* staff, solid-
ified by tragedy and secure in the knowledge of the affection of
the people, developed a new calm. The Ceylonese medical community responded to this with their own new warmth. Tensions
lessened. Festival time was coming as well, and many of our
local colleagues used this as an excuse to forgive and forget. The
Buddhist Festival of the Perahera was to take place in Kandy,
and it seemed as if everyone in Colombo had a relative or friend
in the mountain city. Invitations to attend flooded the ship. The
festival was to last ten days, and it was the administrator's job
to see that the hospital was fully covered while everyone had a
chance to visit Kandy at least once during the festival period.
How Bill Peters accomplished this, I will never know; but
everyone on the *Hope* reached Kandy.

Dr. Tom Bowles, in addition to being program coordinator,
became Kandy's innkeeper. He saw to it that rooms were held,
rotated or crowded with as many as eight *Hope* staffers at a
time at our home away from home, the Hotel Suisse. Under ordinary circumstances we supplied the majority of the tenants for
this hostelry, but at Perahera time rooms were booked months
in advance. During the festival period, the lobbies, ordinarily
quiet and deserted, looked more like a midtown Hilton Hotel.

It is a joyous period in Ceylon and could not have come at a
better time for us. Kandy's Temple of the Tooth is the center of
festival interest. This pagoda-like structure houses a relic revered for years as an eyetooth of the Buddha. It is housed in a

gold casket in the center of the temple, and each year at the
Perahera festival a symbolic golden casket is carried through
the streets on the back of a large elephant. The true tooth and
casket never leave the temple, and one legend has said that the
Portuguese crushed it during their occupation of Ceylon centuries earlier. The true believer does not accept this at all, but
comes to Kandy to make a pilgrimage to the house of the relic.

During the festival thousands journey to the city. Elephants
are brought from every part of the country to march in the
nightly parades. Each night the parade grows longer and more
animals are added. The heavy beasts are covered with brilliant
satins, head and back, reaching almost to the ground and
trimmed with brightly colored portable lights. Only the aper-
tures for the eyes of the massive beasts can be seen. A mahout
rides on the shoulder of each while others walk along side to be
certain the pachyderms will not be alarmed by the crowds lin-
ing the streets. Between each group of elephants the parade
ranks are filled with acrobats, costumed Kandyan dancers and
torchbearers carrying long braziers of burning copra soaked in
kerosene. Drummers and musicians are everywhere. Between
the full moon and the light given off by the torchbearers and the
elephants, night is day. The happiness of the people who live
the grandeur of the ancient past is the real joy. Something happened to us all, Ceylonese and Americans alike, and the glory of
Buddha rekindled the spirit of friendship. It was as if the Lord
Buddha himself had said "stop this foolishness and get on with
the job." Men found a new camaraderie and understanding.

My wife Helen, our youngest son Tommy, and I had the good
fortune to be the guests of the Prime Minister during this festival of 1968. Dudley Senanayake was at his best when he was informal, in the midst of his people. On this occasion he was completely relaxed, casual in an open shirt, drawing periodically on
that pipe of his that seemed as much a part of him as any portion of his body. In many ways, he will always represent Ceylon
to me: courteous, kind, tolerant and loving of his people; a man

with one foot in the past and the other in the present. He understood the necessity for his people to believe in their heritage, and had yielded to their nationalism in ordering that Sinhalese be the national language, not English. Yet, here was a man who spoke with warmth of his days in England, who believed in the practical necessity of turning his nation to the West, and who played golf each morning. Paradox, perhaps? A realist who loved his country.

I shall never forget how he walked among his people, strolled out to a second-floor balcony to watch the parade and waved to thousands not thirty feet below. There was no secret service, no protection, only an assurance that his people, whether they be for him or against him, wished him no harm. It was impossible for me not to reflect upon the different circumstances within our own country, where one President had been assassinated not many years before and where I had seen his successor hustled out the side door of St. Patrick's Cathedral to safeguard him from hostile demonstrators. Which people were the more civilized?

That evening there was a buffet supper, and the Prime Minister stood in line with the rest of his guests. He talked with me about his people and the difficulties which his nation faced. But he was never without a quiet optimism. He gave me the feeling that the country was far bigger than the petty few who gave us concern. He was personally unaware of our difficulties, for even as with our own chief executive, he was well insulated from bad news. It was not my place to tell him otherwise, for he had problems greater than ours.

The relaxed atmosphere throughout the entire festival period gave us considerable opportunity to discuss and analyze informally where we had been and where we were going. The sense of these discussions was well summarized by Pete Morrow who, as the new coordinator of education, had sat in on more informal talks than any three of us. "The key to Western scientific progress," he said, "is openness, receptivity to ideas, even humility before all sources of knowledge." The key to the Sinhalese approach seems to be the relic of the caste system. The pupil respects and obeys the teacher, accepting his pronouncements without question. And while we in America want our sprouting doctors to question our old ways, to outstrip us in our skills, the Oriental seems infused with the necessity of maintaining the image of his own importance. To neglect to do so would be to lose face. A teacher would never say, "I don't know." Yet, an American teacher would readily say this with no loss of self-respect or the loss of respect from his students.

The European notion of "professor," as adopted by this face-saving, caste-sensitive environment, becomes a citadel erected to protect the self-importance of seniority. By presenting ourselves as teachers of techniques, we unwittingly made the Ceylonese professors anxious and insecure. The implication to some was that, as professors, they were exposed as needing to be taught. Their embarrassment became even greater when in our innocence, we "offered" to help them teach their students, thus in their eyes attacking their pedagogical skills, as well as their professional talent. This set up a compensatory overreaction: they spoke of us as being "appalled at their skills and awestruck by their lack of concern for their own poor." But in fact, while recognizing the skills of many, we yearned to add to their abilities, and to help them do more for their indigent by improving organization and clinic management. The political system, while socialistic, still had the built-in political favoritism in which the influential and wealthier had the better of it. People in the villages had told us of their great admiration for the *Hope* but felt they had little opportunity to reach it themselves. The caste system, abolished officially but not in reality, had created barriers between *Hope* and some of the "poor," just as it had between *Hope* and the physicians in the hospitals outside of Colombo General, and Colombo itself.

As we became aware of this subtle operation of a form of caste, we developed our own means of circumventing it. We stopped the useless assault at the walls of professional protocol and sought out the institutions and the men who desired our proffered assistance and teaching skills. Among the less eminent, although not necessarily the less skilled, we found eager acceptance. There was no concern here over an infringement of their "professorial" status, because they were already denied advancement opportunities by the seniority system. Both they and we ourselves had reasoned that this was a happy solution for all. In the habits of the country, those of lesser academic or official stature could accept education from a foreigner with no loss of face. We know only too well that in our own country many of our younger and more recently graduated trainees may be far ahead of their seniors; this situation is in the nature of medicine and springs from the rapid advances of medical science. The same situation obtained in Ceylon, but we never spoke of it.

We knew these were not just our own generalizations, for much of this background was explained to us by the Ceylonese physicians themselves. Thus it was not the men of lesser rank alone who sought us out. We worked with many professors and deans of the medical community who were most cooperative and anxious to learn. Vaguely we sensed ethnic and cultural influences at play. Christians, especially those of Tamil origin, were far more active in participation as counterparts than the Sinhalese Buddhists. Many Sinhalese, Muslims, and Hindus worked cheerfully with us, but the hard-core opposition came almost exclusively from the majority ethnic group. A study in depth of these anthropological factors would have been revealing, but we were not equipped to undertake it.

It was, therefore, after the very frank and candid discussions with our colleagues at Kandy that our medical staff vigorously extended its participation outside of Colombo. They moved into the suburban hospital areas, Colombo South, Colombo North, the cancer hospital at Maragama and the leprosarium at Hendala. Public health units moved into suburban villages and involved themselves more heavily in institutions such as orphan-

ages and schools for the deaf and blind. We sent teams to Galle
and Jaffna, and specialists from these communities came to the
*Hope* for training.

As could be expected, the men at Colombo General Hospital
—the "elite center"—who had previously ignored our proffered
assistance (despite the fact that it was they who helped more
than any other group to create the plans for our coming) now
complained. They complained that we were not giving them sufficient attention and were spread too thin. Within the month we
found that we were regularly engaged in the teaching of more
than eighty house officers and one hundred medical students in
the six Colombo hospitals. Colombo General then began the
practice of assigning a staff doctor full time to the *Hope* for designated periods. These men in turn spread the word among
their peers. Our rotators were sought after far more frequently
for opinions in almost every phase of work at the hospital. Many
professors suddenly became our firm friends. The dean of the
medical school then offered to teach a course in parasitology to
our own medical students on elective assignment from their
medical schools in the United States. He made certain they were
thrown into direct contact with his own students.

The diehards who still felt their own self-images threatened
gave in little by little, but as their stubbornness slowed their
participation, their juniors accumulated knowledge as fast as we
could present it. As far as we were concerned, the juniors were
to be the leaders of tomorrow and part of our function was to
plant the seed of new ideas; theirs was the obligation of nourishment and growth.

Of more significance was the development of personal friendships which became strong bridges linking professional relationships. A new informality was taking hold, and as physicians
made rounds or operated they were now not simply sharing a
stiff professional exchange. They were recalling the good shots
of the previous afternoon's golf or the closeness of a tennis
game. Swimming, bridge and excursions to tea estates became

commonplace. Evenings of recreation, particularly concerts of classical music recordings to which many Ceylonese are wedded as a hobby, created the atmosphere from which true friendship and respect emerged. These led to mutual medical planning, the scheduling of conferences and lectures of common interest. Now, even when some lectures were poorly attended, it was not interpreted as a serious affront, but just one of those things that can happen in a busy profession.

Dinner parties, hosted by our Ceylonese colleagues, became an almost nightly affair. The new informality was the source of many stories, some tongue-in-cheek, some factual. Dr. Rex De-Costa, a well-known physician in Colombo, was speaking one evening of the prodigious number of uses made of the king coconut.

"Doctor, did you know that the liquid in the king coconut can be used for intravenous transfusion? It is completely sterile. It has precisely the same amount of salt necessary for normal intravenous saline solution; and the shell even has three holes! There is one for the outlet, one for the air intake, and one for the injection of any additional fluids necessary." He paused a moment, and then went on. "We really have used it in this fashion, but during the war we found some even better uses for them, particularly in keeping the Americans happy.

"You know," he went on in his clipped British accent and with a twinkle in his eye, "during the war there were some Americans stationed at Trincomalee, which was then a small Navy base on the east coast. We bragged about the quality of our coconuts so much the Americans wouldn't believe us. One day we decided to teach them a lesson. We lined up some thirty or forty innocent-looking coconuts and, unbeknownst to our American friends, injected gin into the coconut through the holes. We then persuaded them to try them and see how good the milk would make them feel. They'd drink them down and exclaim 'Great Scott, they're good! They really do something for you.' Little did they realize what they were imbibing, and it was weeks and several headaches later that they discovered the truth."

It was the same type of camaraderie that persuaded Dr. R. Oswin Fernando, the champion archer of Ceylon, to invite several of our staff to join in a local archery tournament. He was attempting to develop greater interest in the sport and felt that if the Americans participated, the meet would attract more attention. Three members of our staff, which always seemed to have essential hidden talents, had some experience in school and volunteered to enter the tournament. Frances and Deane Collins, our dental hygienist-prosthetist team, and Peggy Emrey, a member of our public health team, were to be our entries. They spent a few weeks practicing after work in preparation for the meet, and then journeyed to Anuradhapura, the site of the meet, as guests of Dr. Fernando and the Ceylonese newspaper *The Observer*. They were greeted cordially and treated like visiting royalty. It was obvious that they were expected to do well.

When the meet began, the three had an immediate sinking sensation. Their competition was to be more than formidable. The most impressive were two gnarled, weathered, gray-haired, dark-skinned men. They were standing before the targets holding arrows quite different from those used by other contestants. They were heavy and short, and had wicked-looking steel points. These men were Veddahs from the almost extinct tribes which still lived in the jungle in central Ceylon. They still used the bow and arrow to hunt for their food, and were reputed to be able to hit anything on the move. But their arrows and technique were unsuited to a stationary target. As the Veddahs shot, they leaned forward and lunged. This movement directed the arrows downward (they would normally shoot at game close to the ground), and their shots constantly missed the target. The speed of their arrows was great, enough to kill a man or an animal, but only from a short distance. When they were urged to move closer to the targets to compensate for their styles and bows, they proudly refused.

Our contestants had no such alibi. A few of their arrows missed the target, but Deane Collins did get one bull's eye, and the majority found their way at least into the periphery of the targets. The crowd cheered lustily, and although they won no trophies, they succeeded in making many new friends for *Hope* and America.

Thus, a summer which began on a note of despondency and discouragement had become a season for the development of a new relationship. We had readjusted our own views and heeded a lesson taught by Buddha himself: "Not the failures of others, not their sins of commission or omission, but his own misdeeds and negligencies should the sage take notice of." The spirit of the Perahera had made both our Ceylonese hosts and ourselves pause and reflect. The future just had to be brighter.

# CHAPTER 18

In one hospital, our relationship was nearly perfect. This was at the Victoria Eye Hospital, located in the middle of downtown Colombo—an imposing and well-kept building with a devoted staff attempting to do the impossible. Its chief of staff had been completely candid from our earliest survey days. He was confident of his own ability and the dedication of his staff. The hospital's achievements were even more notable because only three or four of the staff planned to remain in the field of ophthalmology; the others had been assigned there by the Health Ministry to ease the great patient load. Thanks to the leadership and discipline of the chief of staff, they were doing their job well.

The operating rooms were better maintained than in other hospitals, anesthesia was more reliable and the desire to improve was evident everywhere. They had specifically requested that we provide training in the field of retinal surgery and plastic ophthalmological work. We were advised that none of them felt adequately trained in these vital subspecialties. There was an especially high incidence of retinal detachment in Ceylon, with a variety of theories as to cause. The surgery required for repair of the retina is lengthy and requires special instruments. Although Project HOPE does not as a rule provide gifts of equipment, the instruments necessary for this kind of retinal work simply were not available in Ceylon, and the funds required would amount to approximately thirty-five hundred American dollars.

We were so impressed by the staff's sincerity that we agreed to provide the equipment and spare parts in order to initiate an intensive training program. We in turn insisted they agree to assign only one house officer or staff member for the ten months of our stay to learn the intricate techniques. In the United States such a speciality requires three to four years of training, but Colombo has such a plethora of cases we felt we could give a man enough experience, applying virtually an individual preceptor technique to assure the success of the program. The man trained would then be in a position to train others, for retinal surgery is extremely time consuming and almost too much work for only one man. Without the program, many Ceylonese would remain blind forever.

The procurement of the necessary equipment is a story of rare coincidence. Ray Dinsmore, a close friend, was founder and chairman of the Circumnavigators Club Foundation, which is supported by annual membership donations. Its purpose is charitable, and it is constantly on the alert for small but specific ways to help anywhere in the world. Before the *Hope* went to Ceylon, knowing the need, I discussed the procurement of the required special instrument with Ray, and he became deeply interested, finally agreeing to present it before the foundation's board for consideration.

It was only a few days later that Ray called to tell me excitedly that he had awakened one morning and was unable to see from one of his eyes. He consulted a physician and was told that he had suffered a retinal detachment himself and required immediate surgery. The surgery was successful, and his understanding for the need for the special equipment was, of course, tremendously reinforced. The equipment was purchased and carried to Ceylon on board the *Hope*, and was installed and ready for use within the week after our arrival. One man was to be trained, and many of the blind would see, thanks in no small part to the compassion of a group of men dedicated to international understanding.

Billy Hagler from Emory University initiated our training program in this field, and it was to be sustained by four equally qualified retinal specialists. Old-time *Hope* participants Ford Clarke and Mel Foote carried the load in other phases of the exchange program. They never ceased to be amazed at the eight to nine hundred patients that were seen each day in the eye clinic. Even with the full hospital staff participating, in many instances only a selection of cases could be completely examined. Cataracts were so prevalent that the local Ceylonese eye surgeons were able to perform this particular operation with far greater rapidity and skill than our own men. Therefore we concentrated in other areas of eye disease where we felt we could make a more distinct contribution.

The needs were so great at Victoria Hospital itself that the local ophthalmologists had little time to leave it and work elsewhere in Ceylon. We felt that we could relieve some of the strain if we checked out the children at the schools for the blind to determine if some of them might have operable eye diseases. One of our public health nurses took Dr. Bob Harley, a rotator from the Wills Eye Hospital in Philadelphia, to one school and found a dozen children who would definitely benefit from surgery. These patients were admitted to the ship, thereby not increasing the load at Victoria Hospital.

The most common disorder discovered among the blind children was congenital cataracts. Two of the first patients we saw were brothers aged fourteen and seventeen. They had been brought to the school several years before and left for custodial care. They had never been examined by a physician and were unaware that there was any opportunity whatever for them ever to see, or that Ceylon's own overworked specialists could have helped them, had their condition been diagnosed. These two lads were brought to the *Hope* and scheduled for surgery. Bob did the right eye of each brother first and performed surgery on the left eye of each a week later. The cataracts were aspirated without complications and the eyes healed immediately. Following the second operative procedure, Bob looked into the eyes with an ophthalmoscope and found the retinas to be completely normal. The younger brother had already shown a marked response to his environment even as he gazed about with his blurred vision. Glasses were prescribed and found for both boys. No one will ever forget the expressions on the faces of the boys or their excited audience after they were given the glasses. The youngsters were able to get out of bed by themselves, feed themselves and attend to other normal chores without assistance. This result was to be repeated with others.

The lack of attention to patients of this type is no reflection whatsoever on the Ceylonese physicians. They did all they could merely to handle the patients brought to them at the hospital. It does highlight the ignorance and lack of hope among parents with blind children. Unless similarly afflicted American youngsters are examined and evaluated, they suffer the same neglect. There is an excuse in Ceylon; there is none here at home.

Another real contribution made by Bob Harley and others was at the leper colony at Hendala. The majority of regular eye problems had been taken care of by the time Bob reached Ceylon. Now it was largely a continuing service with the routine teaching of either a house officer or medical students. But one of the most distressing problems in leprosy and its ocular involvement had not yet been tackled—an involvement of the peripheral seventh nerve which prevents the patient from closing the lids tightly. As an added complication, patients had developed an exposure inflammation of the cornea of the eye, and there was a definite grayish haze over the lower half of the cornea. The inability to close the lids like this is known as "lagophthalmos." A number of patients suffering from this were selected and an

operation was performed utilizing certain muscles of the face
(the temporalis muscle) and ligaments within the eyelids. Following this procedure, the patients were able to open and close their
eyes normally. If you don't think that is important, notice how
often you blink, and notice too the strong discomfort you experience if you try to hold your eyes open for too long a period
without closing them.

The patients were extremely grateful. Whenever Bob and his
colleagues came to the wards, the patients would clasp their
hands together and bow their heads not only in greeting but in
prayerful thanks.

Dr. Sivalingham, with whom Bob worked, wrote him after he
returned to Philadelphia. The sentiments he expressed represented the growing friendship and rapport among us all, and the
conscious resentment toward the few who resisted every effort
at understanding. His letter reads in part:

"I hope and pray that you all reached your destination safely.
. . . I hope you enjoyed your stay in Ceylon and enjoyed your
work at the eye hospital too. Please try to forget the bad side of
Ceylon and carry only the pleasanter side of your memories.

"I enjoyed and benefited a lot working with you. I hope I
have not hurt your feelings in any way while you were with us.
. . . All of your postoperative cases have done very well. We
are continuing the Wednesday night discussion regularly each
week and I will continue to do the operation you did for us on
the leper patients at Hendala. I have no words to thank you for
all the help, advice and encouragement you have given me during your stay here. I thank you sincerely for all the splendid
ideas you have left with us. I will never be able to forget you.
. . ."

"Swa," the nickname given to Dr. Sivalingham by our rotators, was among the best-trained and most highly skilled men in
Ceylon. Because he was so confident of himself, it was possible
for him to realize two physicians can always learn from one another. One cannot repeat too often that basic truth: when you

reach the stage in medicine where you feel you have no more to learn, you begin professionally to die a little each day.

We felt that we were learning each day—sometimes professionally, on other occasions acquiring patience and faith. One installation and the efforts made at it brought to us a new realization of what could be done for the mentally retarded child in the way of sympathetic care. This was at Prithipura, a strange-sounding name which means "Happy Place." It was the dream plan of its founder, Bhikku Sumana. It had been established in 1962 as an interreligious fellowship and home for "boys in need of special care," and located on a small piece of land adjoining the beach and the sea in Hendala, Wattula province.

At Prithipura all are encouraged to follow and practice their own religion, something unusual in Ceylon. Staff members, who live on the premises, are essentially volunteers and receive only pocket money for a few personal needs as their compensation. Partial financial support is provided Prithipura by the Social Service Department, the remainder coming from funds received from Flag Day collections, business organizations and individual donations.

The children are admitted for mental deficiency, maladjustment, behavior problems, or on the recommendations of physicians, child guidance clinics, probation and Social Service or by direct parental appeal. Presently the institution is divided into two sections. The babies' section has sixty occupants, mostly mentally defective or abandoned children. The boys' section has eighty-six occupants ranging in age from three to twenty-one years.

The Home is actually a series of cottages divided by outdoor play areas. At the entrance to the grounds stand two statues, one of Buddha and the other of the Blessed Virgin Mary, indicative of the Buddhist and Christian managers of the Home. It had been intended that Prithipura should be only a three-times-a-week stop on the milk run (with milk provided by the *Hope*'s ever-flowing milk recombining plant, affectionately referred to as the Iron Cow.) But the irrepressible student volunteers "discovered" the Home and adopted its inhabitants as their own special project for off-duty volunteer service. Their concern and affection spread quickly among *Hope*'s doctors, nurses and paramedical staff, and it soon became an official public health program. The ship's maritime crew added their efforts, and the children never lacked attention or volunteer help.

Many of the children were badly crippled or disfigured, unable to walk or crawl. Some were blind. The students frequently took them to the beach and helped them into the sea; others were too crippled even for this. The officers and crew of the ship would frequently get together and give a beach party for the whole group. On these occasions they would load the boys into *Hope* vehicles and drive them to the beach, a short distance from the Home. Others walked with the remaining children, hand-in-hand, along the shaded path which led to the Indian Ocean.

It had not occurred to some of the Ceylonese attendants that bathing in the sea would be a particularly suitable activity for these children, but they seemed to have as much fun—or more —than other children would have had on a similar outing. Members of the crew were the first ones into the water, and formed a human-protected swimming area. Others, meanwhile, prepared an American treat of hot dogs roasted over an open fire, cold drinks and ice cream.

Several of the *Hope* staff who had gone along as extra hands were assigned to individual children requiring special supervision. One had a small companion who was totally blind and more than a little frightened at the thought of going swimming. Instead, he seemed to derive considerable pleasure simply sitting or standing silently by the water listening to the happy shrieks of the other children. Later we were told this lad knew the way to the beach by himself and often walked there alone to a favorite rock to enjoy the sounds of the surf and the seagulls. This was his favorite pastime. Although he spoke only in Sinhalese, he was able to communicate successfully with the Americans by gesture and touch.

Each child was able to wring us dry of every bit of emotion. At the end of one afternoon, the representatives of the *Hope* maritime crew made a voluntary contribution of one thousand rupees to the Home, a considerable sum. This was the way in which these men have always tried to be a part of our overall goals and accomplishments.

As for the professional side of our Prithipura campaign, before the year was over each child had been given a medical examination and several had been admitted to the ship for treatment. A health survey was prepared by one of our senior medical students, Sara Ann Cuene, from the University of Wisconsin, and it contained some surprising information which was a tribute to the managers of the school.

Only three of the children had clinical vitamin deficiency, and this was easily remedied. None of the children was suffering from either malaria or filariasis. Comparative blood studies indicated that the mean obtained for each age group was not significantly below normal. Where abnormality was found, it was an iron deficiency resulting usually from worm infestation. Response to treatment was good. The pinworm and the hookworm were very common in Ceylon. Those children with normal blood studies also had worm infestation, corroborating the belief of many that where parasites are common, there is not a necessary relationship to anemia. The height and weight of the children were within normal standards for Ceylon. There was, unfortunately, an almost 100 percent incidence of scabies, but a program was successfully undertaken to remedy this also. An immunization program was set up and all of the children were immunized against diphtheria, pertussis, tetanus and poliomyelitis.

Our most important contribution was the establishment of a complete medical record for each child at "Happy Place." The nutritional study disclosed the diets to be deficient in calories, calcium, iron and Vitamins A, riboflavin, niacin and Vitamin C. A plan was submitted which demonstrated that this could be easily remedied with currently available foods at no significant cost increase to the Home.

The deficiency in our studies was that we were unable to evaluate completely the mental health of the children because of the lack of appropriate screening test materials. Some projective tests were suggested which will have to be evaluated by a local psychiatrist.

With all of its apparent deficiencies, Prithipura is indeed a happy place. The reason is that those who are devoted to helping these children in Ceylon are dedicated individuals, anxious to improve at every opportunity. About the care at the Home, Dr. Martin P. Sayers, a volunteer *Hope* neurosurgeon from Columbus, Ohio, has since said:

"As a pediatric brain surgeon I have worked with birth defects of the brain for twenty-five years in the United States. One of my greater problems has always been to find a sympathetic domiciliary and terminal care for a child of subnormal mentality with short life expectancy. Usually such care is very expensive, hard to find and excessively formal.

"I don't remember any facility in the United States of America which would be considered equivalent to the Prithipura Home. The beautiful setting, clean conditions and calm, friendly care seem to me surprisingly near to the ideal solution for the problem. The children live their limited lives in remarkable dignity and fulfillment."

Here at Prithipura, the "Happy Place," we had come to teach but stayed to learn.

CHAPTER 19

Yes, we had learned. We had seen the capacity of our Ceylonese friends to care and to make do with so little of the material blessings of life. We had come to understand the depth of their religious faith, a faith which was their most treasured possession. Some in our own nation continue to feel it unsophisticated to believe anything other than that God is dead. We wondered how many of those doubters could have survived the trials asked of the people of Ceylon. Without faith, they could only die in the present and not believe in the future. Without hope, they would only despair. Without the love that comes with faith and hope, they could only hate; and with hate as a compelling emotion no nation, weak or strong, can survive.

The Ceylonese people and their physicians had also learned. They had finally accepted our hands in friendship; and, more than that, had begun to hold those hands close to their hearts. They were beginning to realize there was only good intention in our introduction of the philosophy of our methods of teaching. Now they believed that we had come not to humiliate them but to help them stimulate young minds, to awaken the curiosity of the student so that he will question rationally what is being taught and how it may be applied.

As we made suggestions for corrections in ward procedures, sterile techniques, better nursing care, improved laboratory methods, their defenses began to come down. Communications opened. It was as if the "auspicious time" had suddenly arrived for *Hope* in Ceylon. This was not by government edict. Individual decision and reaction had made it so. The ministry officials were delighted as well, for the pressure upon them by cooperating physicians had been almost unbearable. They had stood firmly behind us, and as they understood us more each day, had come to realize why at times we felt offended by press attacks with no official reaction. They explained to us that it would be unwise in Ceylon to enter into direct controversy in the press; that would only play into the hands of the opposition. They were as embarrassed as we were that these attacks placed *Hope* in the middle of a private ideological controversy. We had adopted the same attitude of refusing to become publicly embroiled, much to the officials' surprise and delight. They had assumed an overreaction upon our part, which was never forthcoming.

Beneath all of these tensions still lay the open wound of Vietnam. The division over the war at home was constantly highlighted in the press of Ceylon. The local people, as did all people in Asia, desperately wanted the war to end. This does not imply that the incumbent governments were anti-American, for all of them devoutly wished to have our presence and influence continued in Asia. But weaker countries everywhere dread the use of force. While acknowledging that they were unable to defend themselves, they fear even more the replacement of their rulers by either American, Chinese, or Russian. It is not as if they have the means to combat anarchy in their own countries but prefer to take the chance of fighting their own internal conflicts and in the end being governed by their own people.

We had seen, therefore, a doubt readily created over our motivations by a free but somewhat left-wing press in Ceylon. We had reacted to it, forgetting in our absence from the United

States that many of our own liberal writers were saying the same things about American intentions. It was easy for some Ceylonese to believe we had come to subvert or humiliate them. The man in the street believed the United States had over-reacted in Vietnam. All efforts in private conversations to justify our position in Vietnam were useless. Their minds were made up. Occasional favorable editorials on the American motivation were greeted with vigorous critical response by mail so that the editors had virtually retired behind their desks and abandoned any position of defense whatever.

In this atmosphere, we realized that the best possible attitude we could assume was to do our job well and make the Ceylonese people realize that we were from a good and great country whose only desire was to enable them to help themselves. The fact that we were succeeding was demonstrated by the viciousness of the attacks by the communist press upon our motivations and our actions. Eventually these outbursts helped to gain us sympathy and understanding, first from those who benefited from our work and subsequently from those with whom we worked. Overreaction by either group, the Ceylonese or ourselves, would have been disastrous. The best manner of illustrating disbelief was the increasing evidence of friendship shown by our Ceylonese colleagues. Personal invitations were so many that it became almost impossible to spend a quiet evening on the ship. The Ceylonese had come to and crossed our cultural barriers, and no incident demonstrated it better than the experience of Burt and Ellyn Bronsther.

Ellyn was an exquisite and vivacious brunette who, although of average height, seemed diminutive beside her husband. Burt was a massive man even by our standards, and to the Ceylonese he must have seemed ten feet tall. Well over two hundred pounds, taller than average and heavily bearded, he was an imposing figure. Added to this was his considerable skill as a pediatric surgeon and the wonderful extroverted personality of a native New Yorker. He was enthusiastic, aggressive without being offensive, and had a heart that matched his body. He had come to teach, and he was going to teach. Fortunately, he was assigned to Lady Ridgeway, the pediatric hospital, and was welcomed with open arms. His quality of simply being himself endeared him to his local colleagues. Dinner and cocktail invitations were showered upon him and his wife, and I know that he must have left Ceylon beneath a burden of excess baggage, filled with gifts from local patients and professional friends.

Early in his tour, Burt and Ellyn learned how far our Ceylonese friends had come. The couple already had numerous Ceylonese among their friends in New York who had notified others in Ceylon of their impending arrival, and they were welcomed at the airport as no other rotator had been welcomed before. Their entertainment began even before they were indoctrinated to their duties on the *Hope*.

They were invited to dinner, and a lavish spread placed on the table. Every type of curry, fish, beef, chicken and a variety of vegetables were served. The host noticed that while Burt ate voraciously of everything, Ellyn picked at just the fish curry and the vegetables. Fearing that she might either be ill or that the curries were too heavily spiced, the host inquired politely as to whether Ellyn was well.

"Don't worry," Burt replied, "she is fine."

But the host sensed something was wrong, so Burt finally said, "Ellyn is of the Jewish faith and she is kosher."

"Jewish I understand, but what is this kosher?" inquired the host.

Ellyn smiled and explained, relating her explanation specifically to the fowl. "As a part of my faith, the live chicken must be slaughtered by a religious man who would say a prayer, cut its neck and allow it to bleed to death. After that I am able to eat it, but it must be promptly and freshly prepared. But please, don't worry about me. There are plenty of things here that I can eat."

Her host nodded in understanding and said, "It is much the

same with us Buddhists. Those who are true believers do not drink alcoholic beverages, and our hosts always provide us with soft drinks of some kind. I feel better knowing that it is not our food that upsets you!"

Two evenings later, Burt and Ellyn attended another dinner party given by other friends. Prior to dinner the hostess pulled Ellyn aside and pointed to a section of the table and told her that she could eat all of the food on that section because it was kosher. This included all of the vegetables, the fish curries and the chicken curry as well.

Ellyn did not know whether to be embarrassed or pleasantly surprised, but asked her hostess how she was able to obtain a kosher chicken in Ceylon.

The hostess replied, "Please don't be concerned, it was not too much trouble. I went to the market and purchased a live chicken. I then took it to a religious Moslem who said a prayer and cut its neck. I waited for it to bleed to death and then brought it home and prepared the curry. You see," she beamed proudly, "we can cook kosher style curry, too!"

Ellyn smiled and thanked her profusely and, walking over to Burt, related the story to him. He asked, "Well, what are you going to do, dear?"

"Eat it, of course," she replied. "Anytime a Moslem would prepare a 'kosher' chicken for a Jew, by heaven, I'll eat it." And with that she strode to the buffet table and helped herself to a large serving of chicken curry, the first time in her life she had eaten non-kosher food.

In the professional area, Burt himself did a magnificent job. While not ignoring the local sensitivities, he taught his specialty bluntly, and criticized where criticism was deserved without hesitation. This big, good-natured man made no enemies but gained only respect for his country and our mission.

All of our staff had begun to feel this same attitude of receptivity together with the diminishing of sensitivity. Far healthier exchanges were taking place. Gil Mueller, a surgeon from Ap-

pleton, Wisconsin, was making rounds on the surgical wards at
the Colombo General Hospital. Two months earlier, these would
have been guarded rounds with a minimal exchange of information, with our surgeon acting more as a consultant observer than
active participant. But now things were different. Gil and the
professor on the service passed a bed where a young man of
twenty-eight had been languishing for weeks with slowly advanc-
ing gangrene of the fingers of both hands. Prior to that he had
been in a village Ayurvedic hospital where medications had
failed to alter his condition. Although the patient spoke no English, his eyes spoke for him, directing toward the American physician an eloquent plea for help which said, "My pain is intolerable
and my future hopeless unless you can help me."

He was only one of the more than a hundred surgical patients
the professor was required to see that day, and the professor
had to make all decisions for treatment, surgery or deferral. This
young man had been deferred so often before that Gil wondered
if perhaps they felt he could not be helped but did not have the
heart to tell him so. The pride of the professor would not allow
him to ask for help, particularly in front of his students, but we
of *Hope* had now learned that it was proper for us to offer it.
Gil suggested that there was a possibility of surgical help for
this patient, and the professor said quickly, "Good, why don't
you take him to the ship and see what you can do?"

This meant either that the professor felt it was not possible to
help him—but that the patient should not be denied this last
hope—or that he knew of a procedure that could help him but
was unable to perform it himself, something he did not wish the
house officers or students to know. A further possibility could
have been that he knew of the procedure, did not know how to
do it, but wanted to learn it and could not admit this in the
presence of others. Whatever the reason, he had contrived to
bring this patient before the American doctor and this was significant progress, a sign of respect and friendship at last.

Once aboard the ship, the American team moved swiftly to

make a definite diagnosis so that treatment could commence. Arteriograms were performed. These are radiological studies of the small vessels performed with the use of a radio-opaque dye. These revealed a vascular arterial disease common in Ceylon and somewhat different from anything that we see here at home. Our thoracic surgeon was consulted, the surgical professor advised, and a dorsal sympathectomy was decided upon as the procedure of choice. This would effectively interrupt the nerve control to those vessels which, in the opinion of our doctors, were causing the constriction of the small arterial ends, and the loss of blood supply which resulted from this constriction in turn was causing the gangrene.

This surgery was carried out without incident and the patient noticed immediate improvement in the warmth and the color of his hand. The pain diminished rapidly and eventually disappeared as the circulation came back to the fingers. Both he and his family, who visited him frequently from a nearby village, could not speak their gratitude in words but showered the two surgeons with gifts of fruit and flowers almost daily.

Since the man himself spoke no English, it was a great surprise for Gil to receive a brief, typewritten letter from him some six months after he returned to the United States. He had obviously traveled to the ship, obtained Gil's name and address, and found a Sinhalese friend with a typewriter. The letter was poorly done with grammatical and spelling errors, but as Dr. Mueller himself said, "To me it dramatically emphasized the things that are so meaningful about Project Hope. In fact, in one single sentence, he himself grasped the meaning of Hope, summing up why we as individuals and why our country as a whole must continue to show concern for the peoples of the world."

His letter said, "I SHALL BE THANKFUL TO YOU AND TO YOUR COUNTRY FOR CURING MY FINGERS THAT WAS BADLY DAMAGED. Now I am in good health and ALSO WORKING AS USUAL. I would like to hear more about you so please reply to me."

As for the professor, he had been wise. He knew the studies

required for diagnosis could not be done at Colombo General, so had placed the patient in a position to be cured.

Another example of progress at Colombo General was taking place in the department of urology. Modern urology as Bruce Linderholm, of Minneapolis, explained it, has become a specialty of special instruments and gadgets. The British instruments were of such poor quality and so old that it was impossible to practice modern urology. Endoscopic surgery of any type was out of the question, so our urologists, timid at first, had finally started giving instruments to the hospital. These were instruments brought from home, for the preceding rotating urologists had warned them of the problems to be faced. One of the problems was the total inability to keep even the most simple equipment in good repair. Instead of training people locally in the necessary skills, equipment was returned to England for repair. During our stay in Colombo, for example, a cystoscope was finally returned from England where it had been sent for repair two years previously. No one had thought to forward it by airmail or air freight, so it had gone both ways by sea.

Common medical supplies, such as lubricants, were completely lacking. Instead of lubricating jelly, therefore, anesthetic jelly—which is some twenty times more expensive—was being used for routine work. At one hospital they were completely out of urethral catheters. The interesting thing was that no one complained or even let their needs be known to the Ministry of Health. We decided this might stem from Buddhist philosophy, for it was rare to see anyone angry or excited about these obvious deficiencies. We, however, were often tempted to explode but restrained ourselves. This may have been a disservice; we perhaps should have shown the quiet sufferers an American surgeon in a state of acute distemper at being denied the tools of his trade.

We were at the stage now, however, where the local physicians were at least not offended if we discussed these matters openly. Rapport was excellent with the urologist counterpart and his residents, and Bruce was permitted to select any cases that he wished to work upon. He had found an elderly man with a large bladder stone that was about to be removed by radical, open surgery. This is traumatic in any patient, especially the elderly, the convalescence is lengthy and the patient requires good nursing care to avoid infection.

Linderholm told the professor that it was unfortunate that we didn't have a good lithotrite so we could crush the stone endoscopically. This would avoid radical surgery. The male operating room nurse who had been at Colombo General for fifteen years spoke up and said that they had one but that no one knew how to use it. He brought it out, and we found it was precisely the same instrument used in our own country and Western Europe today.

It was properly sterilized and prepared for use, and Linderholm was able to demonstrate successfully how to remove the stone with this instrument. By an unusual stroke of good fortune, the next patient scheduled on the same day as the old man was suffering from the same condition. Over the good-natured and mild protests of the professor, he handed the lithotrite to the resident house officer and told him to remove the stone. It was a "blind" lithotrite requiring the surgeon to depend solely upon tactile sensation. With great trepidation, but even greater skill, the young surgeon grasped the stone on his first attempt and crushed it into a fine powder all in one stroke. It was the first time in almost two months in Ceylon that Bruce had ever seen a Ceylonese physician express emotion. The lad was so delighted with himself that he shouted, "This is the best thing that has happened to me since I started this service." His professor joined in with the comment that he had learned something, too. They had both discovered a new and simple procedure by utilizing an instrument that had been at the hospital untouched for almost fifteen years. A few months earlier, the professor would have resented this. On this day, he was as proud of the development of a technique which would reduce morbidity and infection in his patients as if he had demonstrated it himself.

Henry Bodner, another urologist, from Los Angeles, had an experience of another kind at the hospital at Kandy. There our program had progressed far more rapidly as a result of the extensive cooperation of our dear friends, Bibs and Dr. Sangakkara. The procedures in the operating rooms were businesslike, the nurses' program had introduced excellent techniques now used at all times. Henry, after weeks of persuasion, had induced the surgeons to allow him to show them the technique for transurethral prostatectomy. This is an operation which is not uncommon and can be performed with the use of instruments introduced internally, rather than submitting the patient to the now-much-discarded, more radical techniques which involve opening the abdomen surgically. The procedure is simpler, the convalescent period for the patient is briefer.

The patient and the operating room were made ready and everyone, properly masked and gowned, awaited the entrance of the American teacher. In he walked with his counterpart, and with no mask covering his face. An almost audible gasp went through the room at this apparent violation of technique. It had been weeks before our nurses had been able to get across the necessity of this operating room discipline to the local nurses.

Suddenly a polite voice, quivering with trepidation, was heard.

"Pardon me, doctor, but did you forget your mask?"

Startled, Henry looked up and realized not that he had forgotten his mask but that he *had* forgotten to explain to the group beforehand that in doing endoscopic surgery a mask is not used, because somehow it fogs the endoscope mirrors which make it possible for the surgeon to see what he is doing.

Quietly he explained this to them, concealing his delight that our girls at Kandy had done such a thorough job.

It was interesting for our urological specialists to have emphasized to them once again the prevalence of British techniques in Ceylon. The British refused to accept this technique for the removal of the prostate gland, although it is used almost everywhere else in the world. For months, our Ceylonese colleagues would not even permit the demonstration of it. But Bodner had persisted, and once the technique was shown, the Ceylonese embraced it and added it to their therapeutic armament. This was why we had persistently insisted upon our participation in what they referred to as routine cases. During the early part of our stay, they had believed we avoided the exotic cases because we were not any more skilled than they. Now they had come to recognize that time, money and lives could be saved by the application of more modern techniques to the routine illnesses with which they were faced each day. What is more significant was that willingness to exchange ideas, to accept techniques anywhere they could be used, was now evident. Professor after professor had left the small hard-core group of resistance and were joining with us in an effort to make the project a significantly successful one.

# CHAPTER 20

In late August a dramatic battle to save a life was begun. Jim Willard, assistant to the hospital administrator on board the *Hope*, was contacted by Thomas Grollman, the Peace Corps physician assigned to volunteers in Ceylon. He asked whether we could accept aboard the *Hope* a patient, a young Peace Corps volunteer who was critically ill in Bombay. The Peace Corps would fly him to Colombo. The lad was so ill that the decision had to be made immediately. They were prepared to evacuate him to the United States but felt he would not survive the trip.

Willard immediately referred Dr. Grollman to Dr. Pete Morrow, who was on duty call as staff chief for the weekend. Morrow obtained the clinical information from the Peace Corps physician and quickly realized the seriousness of the situation. The patient, John Bayne, was in hepatic coma as a result of a severe bout of infectious hepatitis. He had been ill in Bombay approximately one week. He was promptly diagnosed and hospitalized under the care of Dr. Robert Morris, the Peace Corps's Medical Director in Northern India, and Dr. Raymond Lawrence, Peace Corps physician in Bombay. Ray himself was an old friend who had served as a volunteer aboard *Hope* in Nicaragua. The experience had affected him so that he had retired from private practice and determined that he would work abroad where needed in a similar capacity.

Despite good hospital care, the patient had steadily worsened and within six days John Bayne had sunk into a prehepatic coma. Because of the gravity of the patient's condition, a cable was sent to Washington requesting that the young man's family be advised. The Corps not only notified the parents but immediately dispatched a consultant, Dr. Charles Trey from Harvard Medical School, one of our nation's foremost hepatologists. He arrived in Bombay and found the patient in a stage three hepatic coma. At that time, a complete exchange transfusion of fresh blood was carried out, and other more routine treatment continued.

Simultaneously the decision was made to request Bayne's transfer to the *Hope*. With this history in hand, Pete Morrow agreed to his immediate admission and readied our staff in the intensive care units. Fresh blood was collected from an abundance of both Corps and *Hope* volunteers, for we knew that subsequent transfusions, either exchange or regular would be required. Many others stood by ready to replenish the supply should it become necessary. We discussed the best means of getting the patient to the ship and finally decided that he would be flown by chartered aircraft to the Ratmalona airport which was much closer to the ship than the commercial terminal. The Ceylonese government offered a helicopter for his transfer to the ship, but we felt that it would be easier for the patient if he were given an escorted but direct drive to the ship by ambulance. It would not take more than twenty minutes.

On the morning of September 1, accompanied by Doctors Morris, Lawrence, and Trey, young Bayne was flown to Colombo. It was a smooth flight and the ambulance with Dr. Grollman was awaiting them on arrival at Ratmalona. A quick transfer and the trip to the ship were uneventful. As they arrived it seemed as if half the ship's staff lined the rail, for all of them were pulling hard for the life of this man they did not know, as is the way with the men and women of medicine and nursing. He was semicomatose and nonresponsive, still in stage three of his coma. The prognosis was very poor, for it had been determined by the physicians in attendance that more than 90 percent of his liver had undergone serious damage. Now he was in the hands of the Lord—supported by the wisdom of Dr. Trey and the *Hope* medical team—and more than anything else dependent upon the constant care and attention of the *Hope* nurses in the intensive care unit.

When a patient is this seriously ill, there can be no weak link in the medical chain, and the strongest link of all must be the nursing care required for a patient who might otherwise die. John's father arrived from the States shortly afterward and was permitted to see his son. Mr. Bayne joined us all in his spiritual support and almost seemed to transfuse his son with an even greater will to live.

Dr. Trey, although exhausted and without real sleep for close to seventy-two hours, hesitated to leave the boy's bedside. The *Hope* team of physicians joined in his vigil and Doctors Sears, Dripps, Couves, and Diskan began gradually to assume the hour-to-hour responsibility. Trey still would not rest. Instead, he gave our staff a conference on this type of hepatitis and what one could expect and watch for as signs of change. Frequently he rejoined the group at the bedside, holding individual sessions with the physicians and nurses, ever giving suggestions.

The ward itself was otherwise silent, caught up in the same sense of drama that it held during our unsuccessful attempt to save the life of Leslie Kron. Our chief nurse was in attendance constantly. In twenty-four hours four complete blood transfusions were given. Other fluids were slowly dripping into blood vessels on the opposite side, and a variety of supportive medication was given. Nurses cared for him around the clock, volunteers from every other ward on the ship as well as a young nurse from the Peace Corps. So many came to the ward to see how he was doing or to offer whatever assistance they might provide, that it became necessary to call the Intensive Care Unit off limits for those not directly concerned with the case. Necessary isolation procedures were put into effect because of the apparent virulence of his infection.

As the hours passed, Bayne seemed, gradually and unbelievably, to improve. Twenty-four hours after admission he suddenly seemed to have returned to this world. He became aware of people and things and finally understood that he was on board the hospital ship *Hope* in Colombo, Ceylon, and not in the hospital in Bombay, India. This first awareness brought cheer to everyone and the feeling that, barring the unexpected, this battle against disease might be won. Late that evening he received the first nourishment by mouth that he had received in ten days. John Bayne had a will and determination to live and improved with each passing hour. It was only a matter of days before he was asking for steak but had to be satisfied with ginger ale and crackers, for he would have become violently ill on a regular diet. When he began to ask for reading material and to whistle in the ward—either at the nurses or for his own enjoyment—all of us knew then that he would recover. Dr. Trey had departed when John first showed signs of coming out of his coma, for his job was then done. He had helped to sustain life at a critical time in Bombay and provided all of the wisdom at his command to the medical team on the *Hope*.

John's father stood by with all of the strength that only a father can muster. Ever conscious of what was being done for his son, he was fastidious in his efforts not to interfere with the nurses or the physicians. He was at his bedside as often as possible and was deeply impressed with the efforts made by everyone. As always with the critically ill, it was the nurses with whom he was most impressed; no one will ever have to describe for him the devotion of a *Hope* nurse.

Three weeks later John Bayne was discharged for convalescence to the home of Dr. Tom Grollman, and some two weeks thereafter was returned by air to the United States. Now, re-covered, he wanted to return to Bombay to finish the job he began, such is the resiliency of youth.

The drama of this case, combined with the fact that the pa-tient had been flown down from India, had been followed closely in the Ceylonese medical community and the press. It vividly demonstrated our American belief in the practice of team medicine, and one of our greatest desires was to convince our colleagues that their considerable skills could only be fully realized when organized for teamwork.

One area where the team approach was essential was the thoracic and cardiovascular surgical unit. It is one of the finest units in Ceylon, and it was made possible by the driving force of the two or three surgeons who concerned themselves with it. They have themselves specifically borrowed, begged and per-sonally sacrificed in order to get this unit underway. To quote directly one of our cardiac surgeons: "They are standing as an island in the midst of a sea of confusion. They have difficulty in actually accomplishing what they would like to do. They are good students of surgery but have no time to really develop their own surgical interests. They lack a genuine research atti-tude towards things, but I believe that if I practiced in this country the same thing would apply to me very soon after I ar-rived. So many things have to be done in a functional and hur-ried way. I believe there are major differences in attitudes be-tween the Ceylonese surgeons and ourselves. Without being critical of their particular points of view, I would like to point out some of these at this time. We believe in the team effort in surgery. This is somewhat lacking in Ceylon. We perhaps are genuinely more devoted to the total concept of disease. I think we place a great reliance on preoperative and postoperative care of patients, but I think that with the massive volume of se-rious disease which is present in Ceylon—and really the short-age of specialists—some of these things cannot be developed in full."

Those few words sum up one of the problems of international medical educational exchange.

This was the first time in nine years that *Hope* had agreed to provide consultant cardiovascular surgeons, all of whom were experienced open-heart surgeons and teachers, for I had been against *Hope*'s emphasizing such sophisticated and complicated techniques. But in this instance I felt compromise was necessary. These Ceylonese surgeons had sacrificed much in the belief that the thoracic and cardiovascular unit was necessary for their country and their people. They received no private remuneration and had personally sacrificed a good deal to get the program started. Each was an experienced thoracic surgeon, but had received only six months of special training in open-heart surgery in an American university hospital before returning to Ceylon. They set up the equipment, but the team as a whole could not—and could not be expected to—work as our teams do in the United States. I wonder if it is moral for us to train units in this country knowing that they will not have the same facilities at hand when they go back home? I think not; and the difficulties these highly motivated men experienced on their return to Ceylon should have been expected.

Still we felt we must provide consultant help. The unit's equipment had certain parts missing when it arrived in Ceylon, and the heart-lung machine was at first improperly set up. The Ceylonese heart surgeons were forced to improvise, which was not fair. We obtained and flew over some of the missing parts to help them solve this problem. Then we helped to train the operating room nurses who must have special skills and be part of the team. Shirley Johnson, one of our finest surgical nurses, worked for months on the training of an operating room crew. The Ceylonese unit was undaunted by any obstacle, and within the scope of their own culture were to be admired. The open-heart patient is rarely lost in the operating room, however, but is lost preoperatively by poor case selection or postoperatively as a result of inadequate care. No surgeon, regardless of his skill in the operating theater, can overcome these handicaps.

The saddest part of it all is that the senior member of this small group will soon face compulsory retirement, at an age considerably younger than the age at which we retire at home, to make room for another on the salaried roles of government medicine. He was philosophical about this, for "it was a part of the system." When I asked what he would do after retirement, he told me he would run a small farm that he owned outside of the city. His medical skills were so sophisticated, and the equipment he required to work so expensive, that he could not enter into private practice. What a tragic waste it will be to lose this surgeon-philosopher.

How much graver is our responsibility here in America for partially training such a team as this. I do not fault those who provided the training, but strive to understand the need to export such an expensive specialty with such, comparatively, limited use. Less than one tenth of 1 percent of the population of Ceylon will ever benefit from it. As the team perfects its technique, it will necessarily involve significant numbers of skilled personnel already in short supply. Because of the drama attendant on all cardiac surgical work, eventually disproportionate sums of the government medical budget will be invested in its support.

It is not my place to say who shall live or who shall die anywhere—particularly in Ceylon. But so many more will die because there are not sufficient funds to take care of the many instead of the few. It is our obligation to do our best to establish priorities in helping the less fortunate nations in the solution of their problems. I know that all of those who have served on board the *Hope* in every nation in which we have worked return with the philosophy of "first things first." There simply are not enough hands or money to go around.

The obvious answer for many countries is population plan-

ning. *Hope* has long believed in it and has taught every acceptable method of it wherever we have worked. We have learned
as well as taught in this area and found that one cannot just
order people to plan their families. What of the Moslem woman
whose husband can put her into the street if she is unable to
bear a child? How does one convince her that starvation is pre-
ferable to pregnancy? Our method is to bring both mother and
father to well-baby clinics, hoping by doing so to teach them
how to keep the children they have healthy and well nourished,
rather than having more than they can afford to feed adequately.

In Ceylon the problem was being attacked by a wonderful
female gynecologist, Siva Chinatomby. She was a Tamil, highly
respected, skilled and beautiful. Population planning had been
her crusade for several years, for she felt that if the population
were not controlled on that little island, people would soon be
forced into the sea. She had the cooperation of the government
and part of the profession. All women in Ceylon were urged to
participate in the program, and it had gotten off to a good beginning. Then the politicians began to mutter. Rumors swept
the country that the majority group, the Sinhalese, were cooperating but that the Tamils were only pretending to do so in order
to increase the percentage of their minority group in the country. This resulted in serious setbacks to the birth control program.

The Communists, ever ready to add to chaos, contributed
their bit to the confusion by claiming that under their system
one could have all the children he liked. Siva never stopped
working or fighting for her cause, and we did what we could to
help her, which is the way to promote population planning in a
nation other than our own. The people, or at least a functioning
segment of the medical and political society of a nation, must
appreciate the seriousness of the problem sufficiently to ask for
help. The help given must then be acceptable to the religious
beliefs of the area. It is the Siva Chinatombys who will be the

winners of this battle, for they work among their own people and are trusted by them. They know when and how to move strongly and when to relax for a time. But they move ever forward.

Equally important are education programs dedicated to saving lives or making those on this earth better able to contribute something to the progress of their nation. Misery will never make anyone more susceptible to progress or change.

But here, as well, the team concept is essential. Whether one is saving the life of John Bayne, endeavoring to develop an open-heart surgical unit, or establish a population planning unit, progress depends upon a team approach, all must work together for a common end. Siva will never accomplish her aims unless she has the complete cooperation of public health authorities, child and maternal health specialists and nurses and a constant referral service from every part of the country. Her center is in Colombo, she reaches only a few, but yet she tries. Perhaps someday she will have her team. The day may come when our benevolent heart surgeon, the good Mr. Paul, will reflect on his farm that what he began has been good for Ceylon. Perhaps even the Ceylonese versions of the John Baynes will survive their hepatitis because we of the *Hope* have made our point. The individual skills are there, the dreams are there, perhaps someday teamwork will be there as well.

CHAPTER 21

There is no "auspicious time" for an individual to develop cancer. Doctor Raga Cooke, director of the Cancer Institute at Colombo, Ceylon, can testify to this. Cooke has probably seen more cancer, particularly of the mouth, the jaw and the esophagus, than any man alive. He is a man in his early forties, dark-skinned and slightly built. His days begin before the sun is full risen, and end long after dark. Well trained in England, his deft hands move swiftly at the operating table as he works hour after hour to repair as best he can the ravages of this dread disease.

As is the case with so many others in Ceylon, he has little time to spare for research, precise record keeping or even analysis of the causes of cancer. He is tranquil in the face of overwhelming odds, an impossible work load and the realization that many of the patients whom he treats have come to him too late. In some instances he has disagreed with the routine approach to the selection and treatment of patients, but has been too smothered by his responsibilities to fight. He is not discouraged, however, nor is he sensitive. Completely confident of his ability and experience, he welcomes assistance from wherever it may come.

We of *Hope* were fully cognizant of his attitude and had arranged to provide him with a full battery of specialists in the field of head and neck surgery, oral surgery and plastic work. He had requested this help because he was aware that in his haste to treat as many patients as possible he was not obtaining the good plastic results he desired. Unable to leave the country and work with other men, he was sensible enough to realize that nowhere in the world would he find as many oral cancer patients, if only he could bring the surgeons to Ceylon. He had attempted to work out an oral cancer study through major foundations and the American government, but his efforts were to no avail. Had they succeeded he would have had the advantage of working with a visiting professor of surgery for the full two years of the projected study. We offered him the next best opportunity, a variety of our rotators, each for two months. At least Dr. Cooke would have the benefit of fresh ideas and new approaches to his problems.

Dr. Henry Vandenberg, a surgeon from Detroit who specialized in head and neck surgery, was our first consultant to the Cancer Institute. From the beginning, Cooke and he were fast friends. Prior to coming to Colombo, the American had been told of the unbelievable incidence of oral cancer, but he was still utterly amazed at the collection of patients at the Institute and the other hundreds more awaiting admission. The work load was so backed up that many would inevitably die even before admission.

The cause of the cancer has not been definitely or scientifically established, but there seemed little doubt that it was related to chewing betel leaves. Almost 100 percent of the patients seen at the Institute suffering with oral cancer were users of the chew. The five-cent betel chew is to Ceylonese what the hot dog is to an American. Unfortunately the result of the betel chew may well be lethal. It is sold everywhere—in small shops, by sidewalk vendors, or even in larger stores. A fresh betel leaf is selected, sprinkled with areca nut, tobacco and powdered lime. The leaf is folded over, the combination wrapped in a little packet and then put out for sale.

It is chewed much like gum or chewing tobacco and the combination of saliva with the ingredients produces a pink-red juice
which stains the teeth and the lips of the user. Anyone who has
traveled in this part of the world has seen betel chewers constantly spitting. The trajectory demonstrated by some is superb.
Whatever combination of ingredients is absorbed during the
chewing is said to produce a tranquilizing effect and a true feeling of peace and well-being. Despite its narcotic effect, it is
most disconcerting to ride in a cab with a grinning, redmouthed
cabdriver who seems at peace with this world and unconcerned
about reaching the next rather suddenly.

Together with the tranquilizing effect, the juice causes the
gums to retract and this in turn results in the separation of the
teeth. In many users there is destruction to the mucosal tissue
which lines the oral cavity and the cheeks and jaw. There is dispute as to what is the carcinogenic (cancer causing) agent in
the pool of juice. Some feel it is the tobacco, which is suspended
in the pools of saliva along the lower jaw, that is the most likely
cause of the cancer. Others seriously blame the chemical
changes which result from the inclusion of the lime in the mixture. Still others blame the betel leaf. Unfortunately, no public
health or serious research campaign has been undertaken either
to warn the public or determine the deathly ingredient. To deny
the Ceylonese his option to be a betel chewer would be like out-
lawing baseball at home.

Henry Vandenberg was cautious in his approach toward making suggestions, and spent the early part of his tour observing
and learning the routine approaches to therapy at the Cancer
Institute. It was obvious that nothing could be done by *Hope*
staff in regard to possible research and prevention other than
planting the seeds for Dr. Cooke and his colleagues to nourish.
He did notice that routine X-ray therapy was given to all oral
cancer cases on admission. The reasoning, obviously, was to
slow down the malignant process while the patient awaited his
turn for surgery. A concomitant result of such therapy, however,

is a hindrance of the healing process when oral surgery is finally performed, causing considerable distortion and deformed scarring.

Raga and Henry determined to change this routine. The radiologist resisted the change, and was apparently either senior or more powerful in the medical political hierarchy than Dr. Cooke. Raga and Henry repeatedly requested permission to select patients whom they felt were suitable for oral surgery before any X-ray therapy was given but this would have upset the status quo and might have resulted in patients being taken out of turn, another deviation from the social medical system.

But finally their persistence brought results. The radiologist began referring to them patients whom he judged to be hopeless. Soon patients who had been unable to open their mouths either to speak or eat were being discharged from the Institute with a full return of function. The extent of the cancer in some of these cases required major reconstructive surgery. This meant the use of skin grafts, bone grafts and, in many instances, prosthetic devices. But the authorities at the Institute saw many tears of despair replaced by smiles of hope. The two physicians saw to it that the results they obtained quietly established the efficacy of this new approach. Cooke was enthusiastic and greatly welcomed the support that he was receiving. He knew the correct therapy but without our help had been unable to achieve a breakthrough. He had wonderful hands and took to new procedures and techniques as if he had been practicing them for years. We, too, learned considerably from him, for no one could match the volume of his experience nor the novel procedures he himself had been forced to improvise from time to time.

There was an interesting sidelight observed by our doctors during their work at the Institute. They noticed that a relatively small percentage of the oral cancers had spread to the lymph glands of the neck. This type of extension is common in the United States, but on the other hand we have no Ayurvedic physicians. Many of the patients at the Institute had previously consulted these "doctors" who had applied combinations of caustic substances directly to the gums, jaws and cheeks, utilizing the same concoctions that were in vogue a thousand years earlier. The result was a formation of fibrous tissue in the areas of the cancerous lesions, and it is possible this may have prevented the spread of the malignancy. Unfortunately, no substantive research had been done, and Henry Vandenberg's conclusion could only be conjecture.

Our oral surgeons took a young physician under their wing and assumed the responsibility for training him in areas of surgery less extensive than those performed by Dr. Cooke. Raga welcomed this, because he had more than enough to do. The young man learned quickly and was extremely popular with our staff. Tragically, shortly after the *Hope* left he was stabbed to death in what apparently was a senseless holdup attempt.

The spirit of working together had made everyone much more comfortable, and resulted in a mutual facing of the problems of health in Ceylon, stimulating a search for the answers in prevention rather than in cure. At Kandy, more and more cases of a strange peripheral vascular disease were seen. The disease was characterized by a diminishing of the blood supply to the legs —accompanied by severe pain on exercise. Ultimately complete occlusion of the vessels occurred and gangrene of the lower extremities resulted. Tom Bowles and his colleague were convinced that it resembled nothing they had ever seen before. It had always been accepted in Ceylon as a routine problem, a form of Raynaud's disease, but now true research was underway in Kandy. Studies were being made of sections of the small blood vessels and the findings proved to be quite different from what had been expected. By now the Ceylonese themselves will have completed the study of a large group of cases, and a new diagnostic entity should be established. More than that, with the development of this spirit of inquiry, the cause of the disease may be found and there will be far less disability among the

young men. Too much amputation and too much crippling had
been accepted as unavoidable. This awakening of the curiosity
in a physician is the true answer to education.

Also initiated at Kandy was a study of rheumatic fever and
the incidence of rheumatic heart disease. Supported in part by
the voluntary contribution of the Westchester League for Cardiac Children, Dr. Marty Kohn and his counterpart began to
search for the causative relationship between types of infection
other than the conventional strep throat and the incidence of
rheumatic fever. The incidence of rheumatic involvement was
high compared to the incidence of throat infection. Could this
be the result of a myriad of secondary skin infections seen in
children in Ceylon? Studies at home had found little relationship between infection of the skin and the complication of rheumatic fever. But this was Ceylon. Why, too, were the cardiac
complications so much more frequent and more severe? None of
these things had been under investigation until stimulated by
*Hope* physicians. Here, too, it was no lack of desire for research
but the result of almost insurmountable pressure upon the physicians who had little time to do anything except get through the
day. We felt it vital to convince them that only by research,
however fundamental, and prevention would they ever have the
time to live and work as they should.

Dean Bibile and Dr. Sangakkara joined in this concept, and it
was heartening to see some of the younger men eager to become
involved. Their task will not be an easy one, but Bibile has sufficient foresight to know the direction in which he must take his
school. Gradually even the older staff men at Kandy had broken
down. They began to accept changes in routine. In the beginning it had been difficult even to persuade them to modify their
technique of bronchoscopy, an examination which entails passing an instrument into the patients' breathing passages, to locate
and diagnose disease. In fact, our suggestions had been rejected
with considerable vehemence, despite the obvious result of
greater comfort and safety for the patient, as well as the added

opportunity to demonstrate the pathology to the house officers and students. Now, not long afterward, they not only had accepted the new technique but were, in fact, teaching it. No apology was ever made for that earlier attitude, nor any explanation given for the change. It was the Ceylonese way. The converted physician just did something very kind for you to indicate by indirection that now he understood your motivation, that quite simply he wanted to be your friend.

At Colombo all systems were finally "go." The thoracic intensive care unit urged for patients following heart and chest surgery had been initiated by one of our nurses, Diana Stafford, and had long since passed completely under the control of the Ceylonese nurses whom she had trained. As a result of a team effort in the whole cardiothoracic area, operative and aseptic techniques showed drastic improvement, much to the delight of Mr. Paul.

Jeanette Dillman, another of our persistent and competent nurses, had succeeded in completing the development of a central sterile supply center for the use of all of the wards in the main block at Colombo General. She started with nothing and had succeeded in training an entire crew, changing techniques to ones more in keeping with present-day knowledge. This was to result in far less postoperative infection and considerable savings in rupees, always in short supply.

The new premature nursery at Castle Street Hospital, which had been initiated by Dr. Alice Beard and nurse Nancy Fern, had come along so well that Nancy was now able to devote more time to developing a similar nursery at the De Soysa Maternity Center. The local nurses had responded to her training beautifully and were paying close attention to everything from the checking of babies' temperatures to the proper technique of aspiration. These may seem fundamental, but prior to Nancy's supervision and teaching many an infant was dying unnecessarily.

One of the more exciting developments had been the successful cytotechnology training program, the brainchild of our technicians, Irene Tegenkamp and Beverly Watkins. Prior to *Hope*'s arrival in Ceylon, there were no trained technicians in this field at all. These are essential for the taking and examination of smears of the uterus in order to diagnose early cervical cancer. The incidence of cancer of this part of the uterus is high in Ceylon because of poor hygiene, delivery of children without the aid of a physician or midwife and careless midwife care. If detected early enough, the cancer is completely curable by surgery. If not, it spreads throughout the body and death is inevitable. Eight such technicians had been trained, thanks to the persistence of these girls and the eagerness of the two Ceylonese gynecologists in charge at the women's hospitals. This training was to prove extremely valuable later for the progress of population planning programs. When unconfirmed reports were published stating that "the pill" may cause malignant changes in the cervix, many health ministries passed regulations preventing its distribution. This was done primarily in those nations without trained cytotechnologists, for only studies of the smears of patients using the pill will establish its safety.

Vivian Crosswhite had finally succeeded in demonstrating to the physical therapists at Colombo General that there were other ways of determining reflex action and response to stimuli than by prodding youngsters with sharp needles. New techniques of exercise and care were now readily accepted. Her next mission was slowly to persuade them to alter their scheduling so that a great number of patients could be seen. Her efforts were supplemented by the trainees that finally were being brought to our prosthetist so that braces and limbs could be prepared in something under a two-year waiting period.

Total acceptance by the Ceylonese came to us, as might have been expected, from the authorities at Kandy. Several of our physicians were asked to participate in the examination and grading of the medical students. The dental rotators were given the same recognition. No more significant gesture could have been made by the Ceylonese, and it demonstrated the complete turnabout our staff had accomplished by their stick-to-it attitude.

The progress I have described is meaningful, especially considering the short time it took. We came by invitation, it is true—but as strangers, as outsiders who were needed but also suspected. Our cultures were as far apart as the miles that separated us, and our own staff was itself a composite of the varied cultures of the United States. It was difficult for the average Ceylonese to adjust to the aggressive attitudes of a New Yorker, the slow approach of a southerner, the pontifical approach occasionally demonstrated by some of our visiting professors, and the openness of our Midwesterners. Our American culture is a conglomerate and I imagine we inflict more cultural shock than we experience.

Our greatest asset in making friends was always that wonderful white *Hope* ship. She does something to and for us all, and her effect upon the local physicians, nurses and the people themselves is hard to describe. A young Ceylonese lady who worked with us as a volunteer later wrote her impressions:

The distant murmur of the sea, the drone of the engine and the cheerful "hallos" are the familiar sounds that greet me when I climb the gangway of the Good Ship "Hope."

Once inside I get enveloped in one big and efficiently-run floating hospital. Being only a small helper in this very active bee hive, I have plenty of time to observe all that buzzes around me. Most of the time I help at the admissions desk and naturally it was there that I first noticed the way they treated the patients —the old man in the torn sarong, the lady [in] the silk saree, the little child with the skin disease—all in the same way, with the same tender care.

Even the visitors to the ship—the farmer who had left his fields and travelled in the bus, the lady who had told her chauffeur to return in half an hour—the business man with briefcase in hand—they were asked to sit on the same seat, given the same smile.

Yet another refreshing sight is to see our nurses working hand in hand with the nurses on the ship. Dare I say that our nurses seem to have caught the infection from their counterparts and seem to be a more cheerful and smiling band?

If my memory is not letting me down I think it was on my second day on the ship that I saw a doctor's wife carrying her baby with the nanny walking close behind them. Suddenly, I saw the baby being sick all over the floor. That is something to be expected—but what I did not expect to see was the doctor's wife kneeling down and cleaning the floor while the nanny stood hushing the child. Now, isn't that something for you and I to think about.

It is perfectly true, the ship is equipped with all modern machinery—easier ways of cleaning the floors, machines to wash bed pans. But machines do go out of order. What happens then? The nurses wash the bed pans and mop the floors.

A peep from one of the doors to the wards will show bowls overflowing with flowers, rows of beds with patients in coloured pyjamas—some sleeping, others being gently cared by doctors, while the soft footed nurses in sparkling white uniforms lend a helping hand here, an encouraging smile there, which surely adds a spot of brightness to the clean, quiet wards.

One boy told me that he missed the plate of rice and curry. Another said she wished the food was a little hotter! Yet another lady said it was quite a change from the food at home.

Who could cast a disapproving glance at a tray attractively arranged with chicken and peas, boiled vegetables, a creamy glass of milk and a tempting dessert? Or at the grapefruit, cereal and milk they are served at breakfast time? And wasn't it someone wise who said, "Variety is the spice of life!"

If you happen to visit the ship and hear a gurgle of laughter, walk towards the Pediatrics Ward. That is where you will find your culprit happily seated in his cot and playing with a toy he never dreamed of seeing—not even in his wildest dreams. I find it so difficult to believe it is the same little boy who was admitted a week ago. There he is now, after the operation, his leg in plaster, a smile on his lips which must have surely brought a tear of relief to his anxious "Amma."

"I could spend hours watching these little children with their doctors and nurses. They make me think of a home with dozens of happy, contented children. I saw a little girl with her arms around a nurse. Another tiny chap clinging on to the doctor's hand. It must be a little like home to the fortunate kids—and a lot more like the home they want to have to the less fortunate little ones.

The doctors, nurses, almost everyone from the ship, are so friendly that a day hardly passes by without making new friends. Their valiant efforts of saying "bohoma istuti" or "Ayubowan" are accepted with beaming smiles.

I wonder if the patients would still remember after the ten months have glided by the board in the ward which reads, 'We welcome you with love."

I believe they will. I think the doctors, the nurses and all of the people with whom we have worked will know that we welcomed their cooperation with love.

# CHAPTER 22

As the year drew to a close, each day brought more poignant experiences, new friendships and greater commitments by American and Ceylonese alike. It was as if everyone had taken to heart the little sign pinned above a nurses' desk in one of the wards:

For yesterday is but a dream
And tomorrow is but a vision.
But today well-lived makes every
Yesterday a dream of happiness
And every tomorrow a vision of hope.
Look well, therefore, to this day.

Lucienne Lanson looked to Mariyan Mariyan on "this day." The slender patient weighed only eighty-five pounds, mostly bone and sinew, and smiled broadly through widely spaced teeth stained by long use of the betel nut or leaf. As Dr. Lanson reflected, one could easily have passed her on the streets of Colombo without a second look; but to the nurses and doctors of ward C-e on the *Hope* she was to become an inspiration and an exemplification of what this project meant.

Dr. Lanson had first seen her on rounds at the Castle Street Memorial Hospital. She was one of twenty new admissions from the clinic and had traveled one hundred miles from her small mountain village seeking help for the continuous vaginal bleeding which had left her progressively weaker and debilitated. The diagnosis was uncertain, but there was no mistaking the source of the bleeding. It was a large, ulcerating mass involving the entire anterior wall of the vagina. The Ceylonese consultants at Castle Street felt it to be a clear-cut case of primary malignancy involving the wall, and she was scheduled for radical surgery.

Lucienne questioned the diagnosis because of the patient's youth, but the reply was that this condition was occasionally seen in women even younger than thirty-eight. She persisted in her questioning, however, dreading the thought of this woman going to surgery so quickly. She finally persuaded the consultants to do some diagnostic studies, for she was convinced that they were dealing with a type of cancer called metastatic choriocarcinoma, a cancer from the uterus. She even went so far as to bring specimen bottles from the ship, so that our own pathologist could examine the tissue. That very afternoon her suspicion was confirmed.

But this was only the beginning of Mariyan's story. All that night Dr. Lanson tossed in her bed aboard the *Hope* thinking about her. Her personal experience in the treatment of this disease had been limited. She knew from reports in the literature that occasionally remissions and even cures could be effected by chemotherapy. But she had to get that patient on the ship, and convince our own staff as well as the Ceylonese in attendance that the patient had a chance for survival.

Early the next morning the ward consultant, five house officers and Lucienne gathered around Mariyan's bed at Castle Street Memorial. With the diagnosis established, the question of treatment became the center of discussion. It was a lively exchange, bringing out some unusual opinions. Dr. Lanson had already been in Ceylon long enough to learn that she must not exhibit any such reactions as shock, horror or disbelief. She hoped her face would not betray her, and it did not. As she listened to the discussions she determined that Mariyan's sole chance for survival depended on admission to the ship. The Castle Street staff obviously had concluded she was doomed and the treatment they wished to institute required solid laboratory backing and excellent nursing care. She also would need vast amounts of blood. At Castle Street none of these conditions could be met.

It was then that Dr. Lanson quietly asked if she could be transferred to the ship. Her counterpart was more than agreeable and literally jumped at the chance, though he found it hard to believe that we really wanted to accept this patient. But Lucienne had a feeling about her, and we have long since learned in medicine that when you have a feeling, science must occasionally take a back seat. One of the house officers asked Mariyan in her native Tamil tongue whether she would like to go aboard the *Hope*. It was the first time anyone had seen her smile. Even her eyes, which had seemed dull and listless, suddenly brightened.

Shortly afterward, Mariyan arrived aboard the ship, barefooted and still clothed only in her grimy blue cotton sari. She was utterly convinced that she was going to be quickly cured and returned to her husband and eleven children. No matter how hard the *Hope* physician tried to explain to her the seriousness of her illness and the probable need for extensive hospitalization, she only grinned, clasped her hands together and bowed her head. To her Dr. Lanson was her savior and all would be well.

All did go well for twenty-four hours. Laboratory studies were completed and blood transfusions had been constant. But then difficulties began. First it was just a small amount of extra staining on the dressing over the lesion. Next a trickle, and before long a massive hemorrhage. How could this little woman survive? Emergency but conservative measures were immediately instituted with the hope that pressure packing would stop the bleeding. The patient could not tolerate surgery, and the friable tissues in the area of her bleeding would certainly not have tolerated suturing.

For eight hours the battle went on and the packing remained
dry. The patient's vital signs, her pulse, her blood pressure, res-
piration and heart rate all remained stable. Each hour Dr. Lanson returned to be greeted by the confident smile of the faithful
Mariyan. It was heartbreaking, for physician and nurses knew
the odds were against them.

Toward the end of the eight-hour vigil, Dr. Lanson knew she
had lost. Hemorrhage was seeping through the packing and
there was no alternative but to transfer the patient to the operating room, where little chance remained. If only the bleeding
could have been stopped with the application of a few sutures
from below. She tried, but each suture that was set in place
would tear through, resulting in more bleeding. The lesion was
too extensive and the tissue too dead. At the head of the table
the anesthetist was pumping in blood under pressure to keep
the patient out of shock. Dr. Lanson knew she had lost another
round in this dreadful battle for life.

There remained only one alternative, the ligation, or tying off,
of the internal iliac arteries, the vessels that carried the blood to
the area. This would perhaps save her life now, but how would
it affect her later therapy? Once the major blood supply to the
area of the lesion was interrupted, how would the drugs ever
reach the lesion in high enough concentrations to do any good?
All these thoughts crossed the harassed physician's mind, but
she had no alternative. She had to look to this day first.

She called for Bill Swackhamer, one of our general surgeons,
who went to work immediately. Within fifteen minutes the
bleeding had stopped and the last silk suture was in place. Exhausted, Lucienne smiled at the anesthetist and her colleague
and said a silent prayer for Mariyan.

Over the following eight weeks, Mariyan underwent three
courses of chemotherapy and a second operation for the removal
of her uterus. Her collateral circulation had obviously been sufficient to carry adequate concentrations of the drug to the cancerous growth. It was like a miracle. Mariyan's recovery was far

from smooth. Her clinical course was marked by high fevers, severe depression of her bone marrow from the drug which, though temporary, was frightening. There was constant pain and nausea. But while the physicians feared, the patient never doubted. Between setbacks she padded around the ward in her *Hope* pajamas, which always seemed too big in Asia, doubly wrapped and knotted around her tiny waist. She was always helping other patients, and that smile that had first greeted Lucienne never left her face.

Gradually she began to look and feel better. She gained weight and was coincidentally cured of the parasite infestations in her intestines. At last, all of the tests were negative, and nine weeks after her arrival and her bout with death, she was discharged from the *Hope* completely cured. A miracle, perhaps? When Dr. Lanson was asked what really saved Mariyan, she replied, "What really saved Mariyan? It would be logical to give credit to the wonder of chemotherapy and blood transfusions—and it would be only proper to credit the wonderful nurses and doctors of the *Hope*. But I can't help but feel that Mariyan's unshakable faith in us made the difference. We couldn't fail, and it took a frail Tamil woman who couldn't speak a word of English to show us what miracles simple faith can accomplish."

And what of Dr. Lanson herself? She was one of the many whose life will never be the same again after serving aboard the *Hope*. Shortly after the *Hope* came home, she went to Addis Ababa, in Ethiopa, to work with Dr. Reginald Hamlin, one of the world's greatest experts in performing the surgery necessary to repair the stubborn fistulas which occur following obstructed labor. Dr. Lanson is giving three months of her time to work as his assistant without any compensation other than what she may learn from him. This is the kind of person who takes *Hope* to the world.

The uncompromising faith that the patient, the villager, the man in the street had in the *Hope* staff was a little frightening. It was our greatest strength and yet our greatest weakness, for it must have been difficult for the Ceylonese physicians to understand. Roger Barnes, a urologist from Los Angeles, wrote of this to me:

One very vivid impression is the faith which most of the patients had in the staff of the Hope. Patients who were evidently incurable, who had been treated by their local physicians and surgeons, and many who had gone overseas to receive treatment came to the outpatient clinic for screening to go on the *Hope.* Most of them seemed to have the opinion that the doctors on the *Hope* were some kind of superhuman persons who could cure anything and make them well regardless of their disease or deformity. Some of these patients, of course, were not admitted to the *Hope* because it was evident on first examination that they were incurable. Some of them who had disease which might be curable were admitted and most of these, I am glad to say, were helped considerably, if not cured. However, some were no better when they left the ship than when they came.

The absolute faith which these patients had in me as one of the staff members made me very humble. It made me think of the incurable patients who came to Christ for healing when He was on earth. And I wish that I had the miraculous power which Christ had so that they could be healed, but this could not be.

The qualities of humility, forbearance and generosity of the entire staff, including physicians, nurses, technicians and everyone, are outstanding. The people who go to work on the *Hope* are motivated by the desire to help others, and this automatically weeds out selfish, proud and stingy people. The fact that the rotators were willing to sleep in the "jungle," on iron cots, with no privacy whatsoever is indicative of their humility and self abnegation. They were certainly not status seekers.

Those were the words of one of this country's greatest physicians, and a man who has served aboard *Hope* on three occasions. He has, I feel, pinpointed the reasons for the success of our breakthrough in Ceylon as well as in other countries. Faith of the people, and humility and a sound motivation on the part of our staff members. Lucienne Lanson, Cecil Couves, Mo Gallagher and hundreds of others never permitted themselves to be swayed from their appointed goal of teaching, treating and helping others to help themselves.

As the days passed and the time for our departure grew near, the entire staff and our counterparts as well felt something close to panic. There was still so much to be done. The routine teaching was temporarily interrupted by the arrival of the team of examiners from the Royal College of Physicians and Surgeons in England. They were to examine and pass upon the specialty qualifications of some of our younger Ceylonese colleagues. Many of the members of the *Hope* staff were known to the examiners, and the obvious respect and friendship shown them by our British colleagues had a significant effect. When several of our staff were requested to participate as examiners, I believe the final barrier had been passed. The Ceylonese were convinced!

There was then much talk as to whether our stay could be extended; even one of the leaders of the Communist party of Ceylon, in the face of the continuing bad press from the left, inquired as to whether we could possibly remain another six months because the people needed us so much. Unfortunately, these requests could not be honored since we were already committed to our next mission. Preparations were begun for departure, and the round of entertainment and sentimental farewells began. There were official and unofficial parties, and the Prime Minister presented the ship with a sterling silver tray appropriately engraved as a memento of our visit.

But more than anything, our staff was looking forward to the "Elephant Walk," the name that had been given to the day the government permitted us to open the ship to the public so that they as individuals might say farewell. We knew that many would be coming from all over the country, for the people of Ceylon were our faithful friends. They were coming to say good-bye on the day before the ship was to sail. It was a day for the humble, those both in the country and aboard the S.S. *Hope*.

# CHAPTER 23

The last days before departure from any country in which we have worked are hectic and emotion-packed. It was no different in Ceylon. Everyone had made that last trip to his favorite shop and bought the last souvenir. Groups of Hopies intermittently met with their friends in the lobby of the Taprobane Hotel to drink shandy, a popular concoction locally. The same mixture at home would have been the most unlikely of brews, but at the Taprobane it had become a favorite. Many who once counted the days to departure now began to cherish every precious moment.

Aboard the *Hope*, the last of the patients had been readied for return to the local hospitals. As each ward was emptied, the beds freshly made and empty charts secured in their racks, the hospital area began to take on an almost deathly silence. The lights overhead were still as bright, but somehow the wards had become dimmer. The nurses missed the smiles, the gratitude, even the complaints of their patients. Memories flooded in as they chatted among themselves about the many particular patients they remembered: Mariyan Mariyan, who went back to her eleven children; Jainathul Umma who took her first steps on the decks of the *Hope* at the age of four; the two brothers from Mount Lavinia who saw each other for the first time as teen-agers.

In the intensive care unit as they packed away the highly spe-cialized equipment to protect it from the roll of the sea, their thoughts could not help but go back to the tragic death of Les-lie Kron and the equally dramatic but successful battle to save the life of John Bayne. There were so many others, for this had been the area in which all of our critically ill patients had re-ceived care. These girls were professionals in the truest sense of the word, but this had not turned their hearts into stone. Death was never easy, and each life saved was a real victory.

Mary Anna Morris readied an audiometer to deliver to her be-loved school for the deaf at Mount Lavinia. Her colleague, Mr. Cooray, tried to hide his emotions as he helped her. For days he had endeavored to secure official permission for a continuing educational program, and Mary Anna was prepared to remain behind. But somehow bureaucratic delays persisted to the end, and he knew he was to lose a respected friend and teacher. He had apologized and had reassured in the same voice that official channels would be cleared before tomorrow. It was to take months, but we had now become accustomed to the unimpor-tance of time. But Mary Anna wept when she left the children for the last time.

The Kandy Kids—now there were two groups of them—were all back on board, with mostly pleasant memories. Bibs and Dr. Sangakkara would always be remembered. Dr. Aponso and his "new look" pediatric ward, while still not palatial, would remain as a permanent legacy from Mo Gallagher and her fellow Ho-pies.

Walt and Elise Rogers found it difficult to believe that their third year of service on board the *Hope* had come to a close. Their reflections were not only of Ceylon, for he had been chief of staff in Nicaragua and Colombia as well. A montage of faces and experiences passed through their minds as they sat in their

room and talked with other old-time Hopies. Walt had decided
to take a year off, and already had mixed emotions. He wanted
to remain in the United States and yet he knew that both he
and Elise would miss the daily challenge, the delight they both
had in meeting and talking with people the world over. It was a
sad time for them.

The scenes were the same throughout the ship—most thinking
of the past, a few dreaming their dreams of the future. All were
readying the ship for operation "Elephant Walk" and conjec-
tured on who would come and how many. The word had spread
throughout the island, and extra guards had been brought into
the port area. The ship's mate prepared a second gangway so
that the visitors could enter at the forward part of the ship and,
after completing their tour, depart by the after gangway. On the
dockside, workers were preparing the shed, and the same type
of potted palms were being set into place as had been arranged
at our arrival. The public would not be able to see the official
farewell ceremonies, but were at least delighted that they were
to be permitted to see the site for them as they left the ship.

By midnight, "Elephant Walk" minus one, the hospital area
was spotless—with one exception. The admissions area was
cluttered with boxes bearing gifts for the staff from counterparts,
physicians, students and patients. There were stalks of bananas,
every kind of tropical fruit, coconuts by the dozen, batiks,
flowers, wood carvings and every type of brass imaginable.
Some had been taken away, but many still remained, bearing a
touching note to a staff member who had been absent when the
gift bearer arrived. The affection of the Ceylonese people was
strong. The veneer behind which they cloaked their emotions
had been gradually breaking down all week, and now it had all
but disappeared. Many had become as openly emotional as any
Westerner. The mountain of gifts was only one manifestation of
their feelings.

Not many slept well that night, for it had been a night for
packing, reminiscing, and all wanted to see the sun rise over the

bay. The visitors were scheduled for their tours beginning at
eight in the morning, and our nurses—good troupers always—in
their bright white uniforms were already at assigned stations
throughout the hospital area. By seven, many had gone to the
deck to see whether the crowds had assembled. As they looked
over the rail into the vast dock area, there was not a soul. With
a sinking sensation we wondered if the government had canceled the "walk," or whether conceivably we had been wrong all
along in believing the people had grown to love us as much as
we loved them.

We strained to see beyond the walls of the port area, but in
the early morning dimness there was no movement. Of course
we felt let-down, and tried to dispel the feeling with the usual
poor jokes disappointed people tell trying to lift the spirits of
one another. Some wandered back into the air-conditioned comfort of the ship, others were unable to believe what appeared to
have happened and remained expressionless at the rail.

Suddenly at seven thirty the port gates opened. A horde of
people started running toward the ship. As they entered the
broad outer yard of the dock area, they resembled the classical
picture of an Indian food riot as seen through the eyes of Darryl
Zanuck. The group, too large even to estimate, narrowed at its
forward part to a funnel as they approached the meager opening
to the dockside. We felt certain some would be trampled to
death. Adults and children, some running, others carried by
their rapid-transit parents. Some were in Western clothes, others
in the classical dress of Ceylon, saris flying. We thought that if
they all ever reached this ship at once it would surely sink.
Only the monks moved slowly, regally, in their saffron-colored
robes, for no matter who ran or who waited, the religious man
in Ceylon always has the privilege of going to the head of the
line.

Suddenly, from behind the storage buildings came the police.
The crowd slowed with no whistles, no violence but with traditional respect for authority. Moving their arms and hands vigor-

ously, the officers formed the crowd into a long serpentine line, leading from the foot of the gangway and folding back and forth upon itself all the way to the port gate. It resembled a long, coiled, never silent boa constrictor. And it did not end at the gate. From there the line stretched more than a mile to the very entrance of the Taprobane Hotel.

At eight A.M., precisely on schedule, the friends of *Hope* started through the hospital to pay their respects to our staff for the last time. There was never a more gentle or kindly group to tour the ship, abroad or in the States. At each nurses' station the men, women and children clasped their hands before their bowed heads in traditional greeting and farewell. "May you have long life." Some who had been patients or were members of families of patients wanted to say thank you to every Hopie they passed. Others who may have attempted earlier to gain admission to the hospital without success were seeing the ship for the first time; there was a certain sadness about these people, for they still felt that *Hope* doctors could have performed miraculous cures.

As the morning wore on the sun rose higher in the sky, and with it the temperature. The line grew no shorter but there was no disorder, no complaint. Hawkers began to sell drinks and sandwiches, and those that had money bought them. Sliced fresh pineapple was a big item, for it both nourished and quenched thirst. Those without money simply stood in the heat and waited their turn to see the White Ship. Shortly after noon a monsoon shower swept in from the sea, and it rained hard. Not a person left the line, and the long weaving mass continued to move as if nothing had occurred. By late afternoon more than twenty-five thousand people from all over the resplendent isle had made their way through the wards and passages of our hospital. We knew from their faces, from their hands that it would be many years before *Hope* was forgotten in Ceylon. As sunset and then the quick tropical darkness descended on the *Hope*, the authorities at the gate closed the port to the public once again. Hundreds were turned away, but this could not be helped. The patience of the police and the port authorities, the restraint with which the crowds were managed, and above all the patience of the people themselves made this a day to be remembered for all of us. We had touched their hearts and they had in turn reached ours.

It was inevitable that after such a demonstration by the man in the street during the "Elephant Walk" that the official farewell the following day would have to be almost anticlimactic. No matter what the warmth of the words might be, they could not match the eloquence of those who stood all day only for the privilege of saying good-bye. The rumor was out that the Minister of Health had arranged a true Ceylonese farewell, with elephants, Kandyan dancers and the rest. We could believe the dancers, but not the elephants. We were due to sail at eleven in the morning on much the same tide as the day we had come in, and history seemed to be repeating itself. The same shed, the same platform, the same plants and a threat of rain. We again received instructions to meet the Minister and his party at the port gate, this time at ten A.M.

Walt Rogers, Dorothy Aeschliman and myself went to the gate on schedule, and to our amazement found that indeed there were elephants—a family of three, father, mother and baby—bedecked beautifully as they were at the Perahera festival. Behind them awaited the group of Kandyan dancers, dressed as before. Just as we arrived the Minister and his party were descending from their cars. The procession began slowly, the elephants majestically leading the way with their slow, swaying steps. They were followed by the dancers who performed all the way to the dockside, and we in turn flanked the Minister of Health and walked slowly behind the symbolic celebrants. Our staff was standing, as they had on arrival, on either side of the traditional red carpet which led to the speaker's platform. They seemed just as fresh and lovely as they had the day we arrived, although now they were tired and emotionally quite wrung out. The day before had been their day with the people.

But the day was not without its solemnity and its humor as well. The program had been arranged by the staff of the Ministry. Bill Peters, our administrator, had offered whatever assistance he could but was advised that everything had been taken care of. As we approached the platform, we noticed the seats on all sides were filled. The diplomatic community and government officials had arrived en masse. The Minister rose to speak, there was a moment's hesitation, and then he calmly turned to his assistant and asked where he had located the microphone. Embarrassed, the assistant replied that he didn't think he would need one.

Ever alert, our chief engineer who was seated nearby winked at me, and I asked the Minister to sit down for a few moments so that we could chat about the follow-up program while a microphone was set up. A lengthy extension cord was run down from the ship, and a microphone and amplifiers placed in position. The beauty of the Ceylonese—and an added comfort to all who live there as temporary visitors like ourselves—is that a problem such as this is not unexpected and disturbs no one. Thus ten minutes behind schedule, the Minister presented his speech, and it was a proper and warm one. It stressed friendship and cooperation and was all that one could hope for from an official spokesman.

I, in turn, responded and urged no more than I had throughout the year. I took this opportunity to remind the Ceylonese that we had both been British colonies at almost the same time and that our nation in a short span of history had become a great one because it welcomed and encouraged help from all of the nations of the world in the development of our own skills. I hope he received the message. It had been given sincerely.

The final part of the ceremony was to be the presentation of two very large crates of Ceylonese tea to the ship so that they could think of Ceylon evey day while en route home. The Minister rose, spoke of the presentation, and then asked for the tea to be brought forward. Nothing happened, and he asked again. Then Bill Peters hurried to my side and explained to me that he had already had the tea loaded on board and put away. It was our turn to be embarrassed. I quietly explained what had happened to the Minister, but he still wanted to present the tea. Bill was advised to have it carried down the gangway (each crate weighed fifty pounds) and the Minister would present the tea on the dock. I believe he enjoyed getting even over the microphone flap, and while we waited for Bill to perform this function the Minister snapped his fingers and the Kandyan dancers began to perform. Shortly thereafter, two struggling crewmen hauled the first case down the gangway, to be followed by two more with the second. The dancers came to a halt, and the Minister, with a wide grin on his face, presented us formally with a gift of the life-blood of Ceylon, one hundred pounds of her beloved tea.

Tide and pilots wait for no man. With the ceremonies at an end, it was time for us to be on our way. The last good-byes were exchanged, the gangway taken up, and the anchor which had been in the mud of Colombo Harbor for the past ten months was lifted. The long voyage home had begun. There were tears as always, for bidding farewell is always difficult. But the tears were for more than sentiment: many felt that although we had accomplished a great deal, much more could have been done.

The mission was a success. We must never lose sight of our purpose—it is to teach, to stimulate and to bring about change and progress from within. Our own is a fortunate and blessed country, with so much power to give and a great impatience to give it. We must learn still how to give. We know that no one can give more than himself. This is the secret of *Hope*. This is why the *Hope* staff will never be satisfied, and thank heaven they are not. It's difficult sometimes to write or say what *Hope* means to any one of us, and I thought the reflections of one of our volunteer physicians, Franklyn Newmark of Denver, Colorado, told it as well as anyone:

Just before Christmas I was seated alone, in a stadium in Colombo surrounded by brown-skinned people. All strangers, all strange. Twelve thousand miles from Denver, where I live. A million miles from Brooklyn, where I was born. All was indeed strange. Yet, a great sense of peace prevailed as we—all *together*—listened to a men's chorus sing Christmas carols. Carols of many nations. And, at the end, as we sang together, I felt within me—not intellectually, but as a pure sense of emotion—the reality of the brotherhood of man.

"*Hope* afforded me the opportunity of living—not just visiting, but of living—in a strange land. It turned out to be *not* so strange after all. And I shall be forever grateful.

But there is more, for *Hope* brought two other even more valuable gifts. The first of these is *people*. Plain, ordinary Americans, there to serve and to show by precept what Americans are like—or, in a broader sense, what all people can be like. The Hopies, bless them all, from ages 21 to 71, lived in Ceylon for ten months. Their good cheer, friendliness and competence penetrated to the hearts and minds of the Ceylonese.

An example of this was the reception I encountered from the children at an orphanage. Ceylonese children are ordinarily shy. These children at once surrounded me and asked all kinds of questions and showed off some of their new skills—mostly in handling braces. This was my first visit there. The enthusiasm of these youngsters was because of the loving care extended by the *Hope* staff during the preceding ten months.

The Ceylonese are friendly, outgoing and hospitable people. Their social customs, however, are rather conservative. It must have been somewhat of a jolt to see mini-skirts in such abundance. Our lack of consciousness of caste and our democratic regard for women provided support for a change in social values that had already started, and without which their society would continue to be stultified. Yet, because of the sincerity and friendliness of the *Hope* personnel, these cultural contrasts were acceptable. The myth of the Ugly American was shattered.

The final gift was the gift of *hope* itself. Thousands of people —from Ceylon and beyond—sought aid from the ship. A great ferment was created, that there is something better than what is now available. The affirmation of life, in contrast to the Buddhist philosophy of life negation, found a responsive note in the Ceylonese.

We saw an official step in this direction. Under their system of socialized medicine, and because of their financial problems, the government has been providing free but grossly inadequate medical care. It had discouraged private practice, leaving a large number of unemployed physicians in contrast to the tremendous need for doctors. Just before the ship's departure from Ceylon, the government announced that it would not only encourage but would subsidize the entry into private practice by medical graduates for whom government positions were not available.

And what did I gain from this experience?

First of all, I learned to meet, to enjoy and to form good friendships with several people on the other side of the world. I worked with them, I visited with them in their homes, ate their food, and entered into some discussions in depth. I learned that they have the same activities and the same aspirations that we have. Their concerns are with work, home, family and a peaceful world. We experimented with American argumentation, which is foreign to Oriental experience. And I experimented with the Oriental technique of indirect confrontation. Maybe I learned to have a little more patience than before.

I met some very ordinary Americans who are truly extraordinary people, dedicated to the proposition that we must share our talents. There were many obstacles, complications and hang-ups impeding parts of our programs, but the majority of the doctors, nurses and other personnel demonstrated good-natured persistence and unshakable faith. This has restored my own sense of idealism, and has re-established my perspective, both distorted by living too close to the trees.

Another important thing happened to me. I do not know how long it will endure, but for the time being it persists. A great sense of serenity descended upon me shortly after I arrived in Ceylon. Tensions disappeared and I felt at peace. I found I could be with myself, or with others and be content. Part of this, I am sure, was due to the mere fact of being away from my usual, everyday irritations and problems. But there was more to it than just that; part of it was due to living among people who accept life as it is; part of it was the influence of some of the fine friends I made—people who make each moment important, whether at work or play.

This is what *Hope* meant to just one of our staff, but I believe he speaks in a way for many. After almost ten years, what is *Hope* to me, whether it be in Ceylon or any other part of this world? It is the living realization that day after day man the individual, man the nation, only wants a chance to have a better tomorrow. In a time of hate, of violence, I still have hope, because I have seen thousands working together to help one another all over this earth. They have been black, brown, yellow and white. But inside they are all the same, and when we leave this earth it will only be to rejoin our creator who knows no color or creed. He has given me the opportunity on this earth to know and work with some of the finest Americans of our time. So long as there are men and women such as these, giving of themselves to help their fellowmen, their country and the world, that world is bound to be a better place.

# EPILOGUE

And now Ceylon was history—a year to remember, like so many others. We had found that speaking the same language is not always a blessing. Misunderstandings could not be explained away by the convenient excuse that words had been misinterpreted. Thus where there were differences, these differences were clear and polarized; yet in many instances we learned once again that our philosophy was sound. People are basically good. They respond to trust, kindness and an attitude of equality and understanding. But there are always a few who will permit their political sentiments to dominate reasoning and a recognition of what is good for man.

We were to leave behind a dental education team to work together with their Ceylonese colleagues in the development of the dental school at Perideniya. An audiology team was to return to carry on the splendid work begun with the teachers for the deaf. The young Ceylonese ophthalmologist who was trained in retinal surgery was to join one of his North American teachers for a year at Emory University and then return to Ceylon as a qualified teacher himself. Many lasting friendships were made and the spirit of *Hope* will assuredly live in Ceylon for many years to come.

As we departed from that country we were determined not only to continue our work abroad but to apply the lessons learned in almost ten years of work with the undereducated and the underprivileged abroad to the education and well-being of people on our own home front. Many of *Hope's* volunteers had become interested in working among these disadvantaged; and so we turned our attention to the Mexican-Americans and the American Indians. We felt that the Federal Government and many other agencies were already heavily involved in our deprived black urban communities but that there simply was not enough money or personnel to cover the needs of other groups as well. With our vast reservoir of Spanish-speaking personnel already experienced in working among the Latin American underprivileged, we had a natural resource.

Today we are well along in our first project, undertaken in the Rio Grande Valley and based in the city of Laredo, Texas. We have had the cooperation not only of the local authorities but the authorities of the state, the state medical society, and all of the health agencies. We are carrying this project on with private financing and have found the experience an exhilarating one. Two of the community's leading citizens, Dr. Leo Cigarroa and Mr. Jose Gonzalez, have helped to solidify local community support. Our program is concentrating on training Mexican-Americans in the allied health sciences so that they can become gainfully employed and involved in the vital field of comprehensive health care. An innovative Mexican-American culture program has been introduced for all participants in the course, thanks to the cooperation of Dean Arrechiga of the Laredo Junior College and volunteer faculty from the University of Texas system. The great shortage of community health assistants, nurses, laboratory technicians and other health workers, so necessary for the delivery of health care, is known to all. These men and women will not only fill a necessary gap in the health fields but will also qualify for jobs that have dignity and a future. The "ladder" concept of education is being applied so that those who are sufficiently stimulated can constantly improve their chosen skills.

A similar project was initiated among the Navajo Indians at Ganado, Arizona. There an extensive program is underway. In five years the Sage Memorial Hospital on the Navajo Reservation will be operated completely by the Indians themselves. This will be a giant step. It will serve as a stimulating model for other efforts by the Indian population of the United States to improve their own health care. Part of this program is being carried out with the new Navajo Community College at Many Farms, Arizona, and this connection offers great possibilities that Ganado may become a training center for allied health sciences for all Indian populations in that part of the country. Much will depend upon the Navajo himself. We are confident from our early experience that he will succeed.

So the hope that has been brought to many people of the world for the past ten years has now come home. Our work abroad continues with our ship in Tunisia. We hope soon to acquire a second ship. Land-based programs continue in Peru, Ecuador, Nicaragua, Colombia, and Ceylon. We feel the cycle of the decade is complete. We began ten years ago to help people throughout the world and find the same opportunities now to help our people here at home. Hope is indeed the "bread of the poor."

# HONOR ROLL

Abersold, George William, Rev., California
Abrams, Bernard S., Ohio
Abrams, Stanley D., California
Achenbach, Hart, M.D., Massachusetts
Adair, A. Frank, M.D., Minnesota
Adam, LaVera, Iowa
Adamcin, Donna, Ohio
Adams, Harold R., M.D., Minnesota
Adams, John, M.D., California
Adler, Denis C., M.D., California
Aeschliman, Dorothy, California
Agner, Drexel E., California
Aguilera, Gloria, New York
Ahern, Elizabeth, Wisconsin
Ailinger, Rita L., Massachusetts
Alban, Harry, M.D., California
Albrecht, Robert M., M.D., New York
Alcorn, Marshall, M.D., Michigan
Allard, Marjorie, Vermont
Allende, Manuel F., M.D., California
Altrocchi, Paul H., M.D., California
Alvarez, Loretta E., M.D., Philippines
Amromin, George D., M.D., California
Anderson, D. I., D.D.S., California
Anderson, E. Patricia, Nebraska
Anderson, Frederick, M.D., Connecticut
Anderson, Harold T., M.D., Washington
Anderson, Howard S., D.D.S., Washington
Anderson, Joanne V., Connecticut
Anderson, Patricia J., New Jersey
Anderson, Ruth E., New York
Anderson, William W., M.D., California
Angland, Thomas A., M.D., Washington
Anna, Wm. P., Jr., Rev., Maryland
Ansley, Mark K., M.D., Michigan
Antell, Gunnard J., M.D., Florida
Aparicio, Christina, California
Arnhold, Rainer G., M.D., California
Arnzen, Ann D., Maine

Asperheim, Mary Kaye, Wisconsin
Atkinson, Joseph H., Jr,. Colorado
Auger, Patricia A., Minnesota
Austermiller, Joan, Michigan
Bachman, Mary E., Iowa
Baiz, Theodore C., M.D., California
Baker, John D., New Jersey
Baker, Thomas J., M.D., Florida
Baker, Julia M., M.D., Mexico
Bakke, Marlene K., California
Baldwin, William R., Ph.D., Oregon
Balizet, Louis Bernard, Pennsylvania
Bamford, Joel T., New York
Baptisti, Arthur, Jr., M.D., Indiana
Baptisti, Nan, Indiana
Barclay, C.G., M.D., Idaho
Barden, Stewart P., M.D., Michigan
Barker, Lowell, New York
Barnes, Georganna, Pennsylvania
Barnes, Roger W., M.D., California
Barrett, Beach, M.D., Washington
Barton, Lewis, M.D., New York
Beadles, Karen A., Indiana
Beahm, Michael R., Virginia
Beard, Alice G., M.D., Arkansas
Beard, Owen, M.D., Arkansas
Beard, William, Arkansas
Beaubien, Mark S., M.D., Michigan
Bebin, Jose, M.D., Michigan
Bedell, Carolyn P., California
Beecher, Mary, New York
Behrens, Chauncey G., M.D., California
Belohlavek, Judy, Ohio
Bendler, Eleanor M., M.D., Pennsylvania
Benner, A. Norton, M.D., California
Bennett, Ann, M.D., Alabama
Benson, Peter A., M.D., California
Bentley, Herschel Paul, Jr., M.D., Alabama
Bentley, Lesley E., New Jersey

Bergman, R. Theodore, M.D., California
Bergnes, Manuel A., M.D., Pennsylvania
Berkner, Sharon, South Dakota
Bernard, K. Irene, Maryland
Berner, Judy, Pennsylvania
Berry, Elizabeth, Connecticut
Best, Dorothy R., New Mexico
Besterman, Elaine, Ohio
Bezman, Alyce, M.D., California
Bianchi, Jennie L., New York
Biester, Doris J., Iowa
Billen, John R., D.D.S., New York
Billett, Anthony E., D.D.S., Ohio
Billimek, Marilyn, Texas
Billington, Robert, Texas
Bingham, Harvey D., M.D., Washington
Birdsall, Barbara L., California
Bisanz, Annette, Michigan
Bishop, Isabel, Mrs., Michigan
Bishop, Thomas, Michigan
Bjorndahl, Oscar, D.D.S., Minnesota
Black, Ethel A., California
Black, Rita, Colorado
Black, Rita L., Illinois
Blanton, Frederick M., M.D., Maryland
Blish, Constance, Massachusetts
Blomgren, Carol V., Wisconsin
Bloom, Herbert J., D.D.S., Michigan
Bock, Rudolf H., M.D., California
Bodner, Henry, M.D., California
Boehme, Earl J., M.D., California
Boelens, Jack H., Rev., New York
Bogardus, George, M.D., Washington
Bornhofen, John H., M.D., Arkansas
Bowen, Leon M., Virginia
Bowen, Mrs. Leon M. (Charlotte Roller),
　Virginia
Bower, Robert, Rev., Maryland
Bowles, L. Thompson, M.D., New York
Bowman, Hedy M., New Jersey
Boyce, Lois, California
Boyd, Judith A., Colorado
Boyle, Mary, Michigan
Bradbury, Betty Ann, Ohio
Bradley, Nancy, Oregon
Brandes, Nancy E., Ohio
Brannon, M. Elizabeth, South Carolina
Brannon, Mrs. Marianne Rawack,
　California
Brauch, Darline C., Illinois
Braun, Harold A., M.D., Montana
Brecken, Beverly A., New York
Brenan, Margaret M., Pennsylvania
Brennan, Patricia A., M.D., Missouri
Bridges, Joyce, North Carolina
Briggs, John N., M.D., California
Brinley, Floyd J., Jr., M.D., Maryland
Bronk, Anna Mary, Pennsylvania
Bronsther, Burton, M.D., New York
Brooks, Harold W., M.D., Pennsylvania
Brown, Doris J., Connecticut
Brown, Joan, Colorado
Brown, John Q., M.D., Ohio
Brown, Joyce, Georgia
Brown, Marvin, M.D., Ohio
Brown, Robert E., New Jersey
Brown, Robert M., M.D., California

Brown, Roy E., M.D., New York
Brownfield, William E., Idaho
Brush, F. C., M.D., Iowa
Bryan, Burton D., M.D., Massachusetts
Bull, Leland, M.D., Washington
Burchett, Dorothy E., Missouri
Burnford, David W., M.D., Canada
Burgdorf, C.P.M., Jos. Rev., New York
Burgess, Margaret R., Massachusetts
Burke, John E., M.D., Massachusetts
Burkholder, Dorothy D., Pennsylvania
Burnett, Richard C., M.D., California
Burns, Joseph P., Rev., Pennsylvania
Burns, Robert E., M.D., Michigan
Burns, William T., M.D., Pennsylvania
Burnside, Richard Carlton, Colorado
Burtzloff, Benjamin, Nebraska
Burwell, Beverly, Massachusetts
Bushell, Adolph, D.D.S., Connecticut
Buxton, Judith E., West Virginia
Bymoen, Joelyn, North Dakota
Cahill, Elisabeth E., Virginia
Cairns, Lottie Reich, California
Campana, Joseph F., M.D., Pennsylvania
Campbell, Anson B., District of
　Columbia
Campbell, J. Franklin, M.D., Texas
Campbell, Paul E., M.D., Wisconsin
Campbell, Teresa Mary, California
Campion, Ann T., Connecticut
Campion, Mary, Minnesota
Caplan, Benjamin B., M.D., Ohio
Caplan, Richard M., M.D., Iowa
Capriotti, Octavius A., M.D.,
　Pennsylvania
Carlson, Betty, California
Carlson, Oscar W., Rev., Maryland
Carr, Seymour Joseph, D.M.D., California
Carroll, Marilyn A., Kansas
Carter, Dolores, California
Carter, Susan J., New York
Cattoni, Martin, D.D.S., Texas
Chace, Richard, D.D.S., Florida
Chaffin, Ruth I. (Mrs. Douglas Sage),
　California
Chalian, Varoujan A., D.D.S., Indiana
Chamberlain, Naomi, New York
Chandler, Arthur C., M.D., West Virginia
Chase, Gerard, M.D., California
Chase, Wilson W., D.D.S., California
Chasin, Werner, D.M.D., Massachusetts
Cheney, Linda, Massachusetts
Cherney, Paul J., M.D., Pennsylvania
Chessick, Kenneth C., Illinois
Chick, Barbara E., M.D., New York
Childs, Alfred W., M.D., California
Chrest, Clarence P., M.D., Michigan
Chu, Fred Chin, New Jersey
Chusid, Lawrence A., M.D., California
Claman, Henry N., M.D., Colorado
Clark, Edith S., New York
Clark, Elizabeth A., M.D., Vermont
Clark, H. Ford, M.D., Pennsylvania
Clark, Mary Carol, Iowa
Class, Robert N., M.D., Kentucky
Classon, James, Illinois
Cleavenger, Marijane, Virginia

Clendenin, Marge, Maryland
Clifford, Othnile, Ohio
Cody, Robert M., M.D., California
Coffelt, Carl F., M.D., California
Cohen, Carl G., D.M.D., Massachusetts
Cohen, Martin, M.D., Arizona
Coie, Harold Stephen, Jr., California
Coleman, Ethelene, California
Coley, Geoffrey M., M.D., Connecticut
Collier, June, California
Collins, C. Deane, Ohio
Collins, Frances (Mrs. C. Deane Collins), Ohio
Combs, Mildred, North Carolina
Comyns, Joseph J., Rev., Maryland
Conn, Leo, M.D., Florida
Cook, Dorothy, Connecticut
Cook, Sharon, Michigan
Cook, V. Valerie, Michigan
Cooke, Jeremy V., M.D., District of Columbia
Cooke, Samuel L., M.D., Kentucky
Cooper, Alan J., M.D., Washington
Cooper, Clark N., M.D., Iowa
Cooper, Hugh, Jr., D.D.S., Michigan
Cooper, M. Claire, Tennessee
Copple, Peggy J., M.D., Idaho
Corley, Charles, M.D., California
Corley, Margaret, New York
Cornet, Jo Ann, M.D., Illinois
Coulter, William H., M.D., Iowa
Couves, C. M., M.D., Canada
Covalt, Nila K., M.D., Florida
Cuene, Sara Ann, Wisconsin
Coventry, Mark B., M.D., Minnesota
Coviello, Grace, New Jersey
Cramer, Fritz J., M.D., New York
Crane, Edward J., M.D., Massachusetts
Crary, Mary Jo Ann, Utah
Craven, Renee, Michigan
Craw, Nicholas W., District of Columbia
Cress, William, M.D., California
Cretens, Mary L., M.D., Michigan
Crosswhite, Vivian, Ohio
Cuene, Sara Ann, Wisconsin
Cullison, Carol J., New York
Cunningham, Daniel S., M.D., California
Curd, John G., Colorado
Curry, Carol Sue, Illinois
Curry, Linda L., Virginia
Curtis, Charles P., Jr., M.D., Connecticut
Custer, Frederic, D.D.S., Pennsylvania
Czerapowicz, Carol A., Massachusetts
Dachi, Stephen F., D.M.D., Kentucky
Damato, Victoria, Pennsylvania
Damuth, Mary Jane, New York
Danahy, Daniel, New York
Daniel, Myralyn Grace, North Carolina
Daniel, William A., Jr., M.D., Alabama
Daut, R. V., M.D., Iowa
Davenport, Pamela Jr., California
Davis, Charles H., Rev., New York
Davis, Courtland H., Jr., M.D., North Carolina
Davis, Henry, Jr., D.D.S., Louisiana
Davis, Wendall H., D.D.S., California
Day, Mary, California

DeAntonis, Beverly, New York
DeBelius, Lawrence, California
Decker, Harold A., M.D., Michigan
Decker, John P., M.D., Pennsylvania
deCuesta, Mrs. Sarah Thompson, Ohio
Deeths, Harry J., M.D., California
Deerhake, Sandra, Ohio
Dehlinger, Klaus, M.D., California
DelGiorno, Thomas E., M.D., Michigan
DeLuz, Mrs. Kristena E., California
Dempsey, Charlotte E., New York
Dennis, Harold S., M.D., California
Dennis, Robert L., M.D., California
Derrick, G. Lynn, M.D., South Carolina
DesPrez, John D., M.D., Ohio
deVinetea, Jorge, M.D., Peru
DeVoe, Robert W., M.D., California
Diana, Michael A., M.D., New York
DiBona, Janet, Massachusetts
Dickerson, Charles, Michigan
Dickey, Pauline, Ohio
Dickson, W. B., M.D., New York
Digges, Maria N., Maryland
Diller, Kathleen, Texas
Dillman, Jeanette, Iowa
Diskan, Albert E., M.D., Connecticut
Diskan, Lance Kane, Connecticut
Dixon, William Grant, M.D., Utah
Doane, Joseph C., M.D., Florida
Donahue, Margaret M., Michigan
Donley, Joan, Ohio
Donnelly, Sally, Pennsylvania
Donovan, Bernard F., M.D., New York
Donovan, Sarah, Ohio
Dorame, Delia, California
Dorsey, Joseph F., M.D., Massachusetts
Dostal, Robert J., M.D., California
Downes, Maureen, Ohio
Downey, David W., D.D.S., Montana
Downing, George C., M.D., California
Downs, James E., M.D., Tennessee
Doyle, Barbara, Connecticut
Dransfield, N. Diane, Ohio
Drinker, Anne S., M.D., Pennsylvania
Dreelin, Mary R., Virginia
Dripps, Robert D., M.D., Pennsylvania
Drosd, Rudolph E., M.D., Florida
Droxler, Edward A. Rev., Pennsylvania
Duerksen, Merlyn C., M.D., California
Dumm, James B., M.D., Colorado
Dunlap, Edward A., M.D., New York
Dunn, Philip K., California
Durham, Davis G., M.D., Delaware
Dusenberry, Charles, M.D., California
Dysart, Ben R., M.D., California
Dziabis, Carolyn, Indiana
Dzik, Mary Ann, Illinois
Eberle, Robert C., M.D., Illinois
Edmunds, David W., Rev., Texas
Edwards, Doris Anne, Pennsylvania
Edwards, Sterling, M.D., Alabama
Ehlert, William, Alabama
Eiman, John W., M.D., Pennsylvania
Eisenhart, M. Evelyn, Maryland
Elias, Ralph B., M.D., California
Elliott, Barbara Ann, Virginia
Elliott, Richard O., M.D., Massachusetts

Elliott, Robert, D.D.S., California
Ellis, Eldon E., M.D., California
Elmore, Mary, Colorado
Emrey, Margaret, Pennsylvania
Endress, Mary P., Michigan
England, Barbara, North Carolina
English, Woodruff Jones, II, New Jersey
Ennis, LeRoy M., D.D.S., Pennsylvania
Enright, James, Canada
Epstein, Joseph A., M.D., New York
Ergin, Nevit O., M.D., Michigan
Erickson, Barbara J., Washington
Erickson, Carl A., M.D., California
Essenmacher, Doreen, Michigan
Etzwiler, Donnel D., M.D., Minnesota
Faber, Kalman, M.D., Pennsylvania
Fager, Charles A., M.D., Massachusetts
Fakkema, LaVerne, California
Falces, Edward, M.D., California
Falces, Frances, M.D., California
Falck, Frank J., Ph.D., Vermont
Falck, Vilma T., Ph.D., Vermont
Fangman, Anne M., Nebraska
Fardelmann, Dale von Prief, M.D.,
  New Hampshire
Farley, Barbara, New York
Farrington, Charles, M.D., Florida
Fearl, Clifford, L., M.D., Oregon
Feeney, Kathleen Agnes, Colorado
Feigelson, Howard, M.D., Michigan
Fern, Nancy, Florida
Fernbach, L. Virginia, New York
Ferreira, Genevieve, California
Ferrin, John W., M.D., California
Feuer, Abe Lawrence, M.D., North
  Carolina
Fiddes, Barbara E., Connecticut
Fifer, John S., M.D., Florida
Finlay, John R., M.D., Connecticut
Finlay, Vera M., M.D., Connecticut
Finley, Mary Ellen, California
Fisher, Benjamin Kopel, M.D., Canada
Fisher, John J., M.D., Florida
Fishman, Donald Jay, M.D., Ohio
Fishman, Ronald S., M.D., Maryland
Flanigan, Stevenson, M.D., Connecticut
Fleetwood, Lyman A., D.D.S., Washington
Flege, John B., Jr., M.D., Iowa
Fleming, Richard Eliot, Jr., New Jersey
Fleming, William L., M.D., North
  Carolina
Fleuchaus, Philip T., D.D.S., Florida
Flynn, Mary, New Jersey
Folcik, Pauline, Michigan
Foley, Patricia, Massachusetts
Folger, William S., M.D., California
Folsom, Clarence H., M.D., California
Foltz, Mary Louise, New York
Fooks, Doris, Kentucky
Foote, C. M., M.D., Nebraska
Footer, Wilson, M.D., California
Ford, John L., M.D., Arizona
Forsythe, Paul J., Rev., Virginia
Foti, Ignatia, New York
Fountain, Edmund M., M.D., Texas
Frank, Sister Charles Marie, District
  of Columbia

Franzblau, M. J., M.D., California
Fraser, Mary A., California
Frerichs, Douglas W., M.D., Arizona
Freshman, Michael Earl, M.D., California
Frevert, Elaine, Iowa
Friedman, Eugene, D.D.S., New York
Fritz, Lois Ann, District of Columbia
Fuller, Jean, Iowa
Furnas, David W., M.D., Iowa
Gaines, Richard R., D.D.S., Florida
Gaiser, Judith F., District of Columbia
Gallagher, Maureen, Rhode Island
Gallagher, Mary L., California
Gallagher, Wm. B., M.D., Wisconsin
Garber, Pauline E., M.D., Ohio
Garson, C. H., D.D.S., California
Gass, H. Harvey, M.D., Michigan
Gavran, Kathleen S., California
Geissler, Elaine, California
Geoghegan, Ann, Ohio
Geraci, Charles L., M.D., California
Gerber, Alex., M.D., California
Gerber, Edward P., M.D., California
Gering, Stanley A., California
Geuting, Joseph T., III, Maryland
Gianotti, E. F., M.D., California
Gibson, Henry H., M.D., Ohio
Gingles, Carle E., D.D.S., Michigan
Glass, Bernard, M.D., Ohio
Glocke, Susan B., California
Glover, Mary A., M.D., Hawaii
Goble, Joan, M.D., California
Goble, John, M.D., California
Godley, David Robert, California
Goiney, Bernard J., M.D., Washington
Golden, Archie S., M.D., Connecticut
Golden, Sylvia, Connecticut
Golbuff, Judith, Iowa
Goler, George G., M.D., Ohio
Goodsell, John, M.D., Michigan
Goodwin, Bonnie E., Michigan
Gordon, Harold N., M.D., Arizona
Gordon, Howard L., M.D., Florida
Gordon, Richard D., Florida
Gorman, Fred E., M.D., New York
Gorney, Mark, M.D., California
Gotten, Nicholas, M.D., Tennessee
Gouge, Ruth L., M.D., Colorado
Gould, John M., M.D., California
Graf, Carl M., M.D., New York
Graham, Gail E., Vermont
Greathead, R. Scott, California
Green, Carl A., M.D., Alabama
Green, Charles E., M.D., Oklahoma
Green, Richard K., D.D.S., Virginia
Greene, Dennis Alan, Illinois
Greenfield, Larry, California
Griffith, John B., M.D., Colorado
Griffiths, Norman H. C., D.D.S., District
  of Columbia
Griggs, Gordon P., M.D., California
Grimes, Dorothy, Connecticut
Grodsky, Pauline, M.D., Tennessee
Grossman, Tina, New York
Guilford, Arthur, Ohio
Gunn, Edward, Jr., Maryland
Gurewitsch, Arno, M.D., New York

Guthrie, James, M.D., Arkansas
Guynn, James, Virginia
Haber, Seymour, M.D., Oregon
Hadley, Henry, M.D., California
Haerer, Armin, M.D., Mississippi
Hagler, William S., M.D., Georgia
Hagwood, Daniel S., M.D., Alabama
Hahn, George A., M.D., Pennsylvania
Hahn, Richard S., M.D., California
Haines, Gerald L., M.D., New York
Hale, Merle, D.D.S., Iowa
Hall, Harry B., M.D., Minnesota
Hall, William T., M.D., California
Hamel, Neal C., M.D., California
Hamilton, Edwin B., M.D., Ohio
Hamilton, Quentin P., M.D., Michigan
Hammond, Donald R., M.D., Washington
Hammond, Elizabeth M., California
Hammond, Gloria B., California
Hanan, Robert, M.D., Arizona
Hanford, Charles W., M.D., California
Hannum, Thomas L., M.D., Utah
Hansen, Inge Marie, Denmark
Hansen, James R., M.D., California
Harden, Jessie D., Rev., California
Harder, Herbert I., M.D., California
Hardison, Samuel H., D.D.S., Tennessee
Hardy, William W., Jr., M.D., Michigan
Hark, Bernard, M.D., California
Harley, Robison D., M.D., Pennsylvania
Harmon, Frankie L., California
Harness, Wm. N., M.D., California
Harris, Frances M., Texas
Harris, J. Mayfield, M.D., California
Harris, Jacqueline, Ohio
Harris, James H., M.D., Oregon
Harris, W. Andrew, Virginia
Harrison, Lee-Olive, Washington
Harrison, R. S., M.D., California
Hashizume, Sato, Oregon
Hastedt, Robert C., M.D., Ohio
Hawkes, C. Douglas, M.D., Tennessee
Hayashi, Donald T., M.D., California
Hayes, Thomas H., M.D., California
Haynes, Walter M., M.D., Ohio
Hazelrigg, Thomas R., Jr., M.D., Washington
Hecker, Linda, Minnesota
Heersema, Philip H., M.D., California
Hefelfinger, Joanne, California
Heffner, Leonard T., Jr., North Carolina
Heiligman, Sol J., D.D.S., New York
Heim, David J., Rev., Vermont
Helfer, Lewis M., M.D., Texas
Helldorfer, N., Rev., Maryland
Hellman, Stanley, D.D.S., California
Hellwig, Randolph B., Rev., New York
Hemighaus, Joseph, Rev., Pennsylvania
Henderek, Martha, Canada
Hendrick, Carol L., Michigan
Heneveld, Edward H., M.D., Michigan
Hennessy, James J., M.D., Connecticut
Hennessy, Richard J., Michigan
Henning, Phyllis I., Washington
Henry, John C., Rev., Virginia
Hentz, Dorcas R., Montana
Heppe, Clarence, California

Herget, Charles J., Rev., Pennsylvania
Herrera, Christine, Colorado
Herrman, S. F., M.D., Washington
Hershey, William N., M.D., New Mexico
Hershey, Barbara A., M.D., New Mexico
Hester, Elsie, Massachusetts
Hester, Elfreda E., Massachusetts
Hicks, Mrs. Lory, California
Hiebert, Clement A., M.D., Maine
Hill, Malcolm R., Sr., M.D., California
Hines, Peter, Rev., Vermont
Hinoki, Earsei, California
Hirsch, Annette M., New Jersey
Hirschfelder, Max, M.D., Illinois
Hite, Alice J., Ohio
Hoagland, Terrence V., Michigan
Hodges, Frank V., M.D., Michigan
Hodgson, Jane, M.D. (Mrs. Frank Quattlebaum), Minnesota
Hodkinson, Barbara A., Pennsylvania
Hoerner, Virginia L., California
Hoffman, Howard A., M.D., Massachusetts
Holcomb, Carmen, Washington
Holder, Davine Ann, Missouri
Holleman, Jane B., Georgia
Homer, Ann M., New York
Hoover, Lorna (Mrs. Walter B.), Florida
Hoover, Norman W., M.D., Minnesota
Hopkins, Mary, Ohio
Hopple, Lynwood M., M.D., Colorado
Horak, Ruth A., Pennsylvania
Horton, Robert, M.D., California
Horwich, Harry, M.D., Florida
Houde, Maurice, D.D.S., Canada
Hovsepian, Deron, M.D., California
Howard, Allan H., M.D., California
Howard, Ruth I., Maryland
Howell, James P., Michigan
Hoyt, Katherine C., Washington
Hubbell, Adrian O., D.D.S., California
Hudson, James I., Jr., M.D., Maryland
Hudson, Paul, M.D., Maryland
Hufnagel, Charles A., M.D., District of Columbia
Hughes, Calvin T., M.D., Connecticut
Hughes, Mary Lilian, Massachusetts
Hull, Forrest E., M.D., California
Hultgen, William J., M.D., California
Hunger, Joan, California
Hunt, James C., M.D., Illinois
Hunt, William E., M.D., Ohio
Huntington, Catherine, Pennsylvania
Hurd, Brooks, M.D., Ohio
Hurteau, Everett F., M.D., Ohio
Hurwitz, Alfred, M.D., Florida
Huston, John, Jr., M.D., Iowa
Imbriglia, Joseph E., M.D., Pennsylvania
Ippolito, Nicholas A., D.D.S., New York
Ireton, Richard J., M.D., Ohio
Isaac, Charles A., M.D., Kansas
Iverson, Leigh I. G., Wisconsin
Ives, Elinor R., M.D., California
Jacobsen, Hart, Illinois
James, Alice McLean, New York
Janda, George W., M.D., Minnesota
Jansen, Donald H., M.D., Ohio
Jeanes, Darlene, Indiana

Jene, Joanne, M.D., Oregon
Jennings, Kenneth, Jr., M.D., Minnesota
Jensen, Marshall N., M.D., Florida
Jerofke, Alfred, M.D., Wisconsin
Jessop, Karen B., Rhode Island
Jobe, James P., M.D., Oklahoma
Johanson, Audrey Kay, California
Johner, Carl, M.D., Illinois
Johnson, L. Morris, M.D., California
Johnson, Newell A., M.D., California
Johnson, Paul, M.D., Washington
Johnson, Shirley, Minnesota
Johnson, Virginia, California
Johnson, Wallace, D.D.S., Iowa
Johnson, Joan (Mrs. Walter), California
Johnson, Walter, M.D., California
Jones, Edward G., M.D., California
Jones, Howard L., M.D., California
Jones, Theodore Winslow, M.D.,
  Massachusetts
Jordan, Harriet, California
Jordan, Hugh E., M.D., California
Junkerman, Charles L., M.D., Wisconsin
Kabacy, George E., California
Kagan, Martin B., D.D.S., New York
Kanter, Albert J., M.D., California
Karam, Adib, M.D., New York
Kaufman, Karolyn, Illinois
Kaufman, Myron, D.D.S., Michigan
Kaufman, Sally (Mrs. Myron), Michigan
Kauffman, Raymond R., M.D., California
Kavanaugh, Harry M., D.D.S., Michigan
Keedy, Christian. M.D., Florida
Keeley, Kim A., M.D., New York
Keener, Sunday L., Ohio
Kegel. Richard F. C., M.D., New York
Kell, George, District of Columbia
Kelley, Charles B., D.D.S., South-Dakota
Kelley, Margaret D., Massachusetts
Kellogg, Robert O., M.D., Maine
Kennedy, Robert E., M.D., New York
Kennedy, Mary Frances, California
Kennedy, Walter W., New York
Kerman, Herbert D., M.D., Florida
Kerr, Frederick W. L., M.D., Minnesota
Kerr, S. E., M.D., Ohio
Kerr, Walter S., M.D., Massachusetts
Kester, Nancy, M.D., New York
Kielts, Theodore, D.D.S., Michigan
Kilpatrick, Jeanne, Illinois
King, Rufus Gunn, III, Maryland
King, Stanley A., Michigan
Kinsling, Harry, M.D., California
Kiolet, Margaret E., Montana
Kirchdoerfer, H., M.D., California
Kirchheim, Dieter, M.D., Oregon
Kirkendall, Guy R., M.D., District of
  Columbia
Kirkland, T. N., Jr., M.D., Alabama
Kirn, George J., M.D., California
Kitchin, James D., III, M.D., Virginia
Klein, Louise K., Pennsylvania
Klein, Monique, District of Columbia
Klein, Philip M., M.D., California
Klish, William John, Wisconsin
Klumpp, Maria M., New York
Knake, George W., Jr., M.D., South Dakota

Knighton, Robert, M.D., Michigan
Knights, Edwin M., Jr., M.D., Michigan
Knights, Ruth Carrie, Michigan
Kohls, Rose K., South Dakota
Kohn, Jean, M.D., (Mrs. Martin M.),
  California
Kohn, Martin M., M.D., California
Kostoss, Ann Marie, Connecticut
Kramer, Bernard M., M.D., California
Kogan, Stanley, D.D.S., Maryland
Kohner, Dinah, M.D., Ireland
Kradjian, Christine S. (Mrs. Robert M),
  California
Kradjian, Robert M., M.D., California
Krasner, Bernard, M.D., Massachusetts
Krauss, Audrey, M.D., Pennsylvania
Kremer, Howard U., M.D., Pennsylvania
Kremer, William F., M.D., New York
Kretchmar, Joseph S., M.D., Wisconsin
Krol, Mary Ann, Illinois
Kron, Samuel D., M.D., Pennsylvania
Kronschnabel, Edward F., M.D., Michigan
Krueger, Carol Grace, Illinois
Kuharic, Henry, M.D., Washington
Kuhn, Mark A. R., M.D., Florida
Kuhn, Walter, W., C.S.S.R., New York
Kushwara, Barbara, Pennsylvania
Kyle, Sally C., Massachusetts
Lack, Herbert, M.D., California
Lally, Timothy F., M.D., California
Lamphere, Lottie, Michigan
Lane, Mary Lou, Washington
Langer, Catherine, Illinois
Langston, J. D., M.D., Michigan
Langston, James William, Missouri
Lanson, Lucienne T., M.D., Pennsylvania
La Porta, Michael, M.D., New Jersey
Larison, Patricia J., Alabama
LaRose-Saurette, Joseph Edgar W. F.,
  New Jersey
Lashmet, Michael H., M.D., Indiana
Lawler, Dolores, New York
Lawlor, Jeremiah Francis, M.D., New
  York
Lawlor, Virginia E., Iowa
Lawrence, Montague, M.D., Iowa
Lawrence, Raymond W., M.D., New
  Hampshire
Lawrence, Sylvia, Massachusetts
Lawson, Phillip S., West Virginia
Layman, Mary, California
le Brocquy, Jean, M.D., Ireland
LeCheminant, Wilford H., M.D., Utah
LeCocq, John F., M.D., Washington
Lee, Tami, California
Leeming, Joan, M.D., New York
Lehan, Barbara L., Tennessee
Lehmann, J. H., M.D., Washington
Lehmann, Peter O., M.D., Canada
Lehrer, Melinda E., California
Leider, Jon F., Wisconsin
Lekas, Mary D., M.D., Rhode Island
Leland, Carol M., M.D., California
Leman, Craig, M.D., Oregon
Lenel, Rosemarie M., M.D., California
Lentino, Walter, M.D., New York
Lenzmeier, A. Ann, Minnesota

Leo, Thomas F., M.D., New York
Lesko, Geraldine (Mrs. Louis), California
Lesko, Louis, M.D., California
Levin, Carol M., Pennsylvania
Lewis, Annette, Florida
Lewis, David T., M.D., Kentucky
Lewis, Gary, Virginia
Lewis, Sally A., Pennsylvania
Liebowitz, Daniel, M.D., California
Liechty, R. D., M.D., Iowa
Lillard, Richard L., M.D., Washington
Linden, Jack L., M.D., New York
Linderholm, Bruce E., M.D., Minnesota
Lindholm, Inger M., Iowa
Lindley, Sheldon K., M.D., California
Lindquist, M. F., M.D., Minnesota
Lipsey, James H., Jr., M.D., Tennessee
Lisman, Jack V., M.D., New York
Lloyd, Stacy B., District of Columbia
Loehning, Robert, M.D., Utah
Loeser, Eugene, M.D., New Jersey
Logue, John T., M.D., Missouri
Long, Albert E., M.D., California
Longman, Alice J., New York
Lover, James, Rev., New York
Lowry, Robert, M.D., Michigan
Lowther, Laura R., Ohio
Lukasik, Claudette, Wisconsin
Ludwig, Ninalee H., Ohio
Lussier, Suzanne M., Canada
Lutz, Velma, Ohio
Luz, Lester A., M.D., California
Macer, George A., M.D., California
Macgregor, Charles A., M.D.,
    Massachusetts
MacGregor, John K., M.D., Iowa
Mack, Elaine E., Ohio
Mackey, Harry E., M.D., Oregon
MacLean, Donald, Canada
Madison, James B., M.D., Florida
Maeck, John Van Sicklen, M.D., Vermont
Maggiore, Edward D., D.D.S., California
Magner, S. J., John F., Rev., California
Malik, Nancy, California
Maloney, Dolores, New York
Manion, Ruth, California
Mann, Joseph M., III, Michigan
Manwell, Claire Cutten, M.D.,
    Massachusetts
Manwell, Edward J., M.D., Massachusetts
March, Harriet Seipel, California
Margold, Allen M., M.D., Connecticut
Margolis, Alan J., M.D., California
Mark, Richard S., New York
Marks, Richard M., M.D., California
Martin, S. Lawrence, Jr., Kansas
Martin, Joan, Kansas
Mason, Thomas H., M.D., New York
Mathewson, Eleanor, California
Matte, Michael L., M.D., California
Matteis, Joice C., Connecticut
Matthews, B. Ellen, District of Columbia
Mayall, Stanley E., D.D.S., Washington
McBratney, J. Greer, M.D., Massachusetts
McBride, Robert H., M.D., Iowa
McCabe, Judith E., California
McCafferty, William, M.D., Pennsylvania

McCannell, Malcolm A., M.D., Minnesota
McCarthy, Ann R., New York
McClintock, Everett, M.D., Arkansas
McConnell, Bernie A., D.D.S., Ohio
McConnell, Dona, Ohio
McCort, James, M.D., California
McCutcheon, Sue A., M.D., Michigan
McDermott, John, M.D., California
McDiarmid, Grover W., Virginia
McDonald, Jean, California
McDonald, Maurice, Rev., New York
McDonald, William, M.D., Montana
McDonnell, D. P., M.D., California
McDonough, John, M.D., Ohio
McGee, Charles T., M.D., Louisiana
McGee, Carole J., Louisiana
McGreal, Patrick J., California
McGuire, Philip R., M.D., Illinois
McIntyre, Eleanor, Michigan
McKenzie, Kenneth R., M.D., California
McKinney, Brenda, North Carolina
McKinney, Frederick M., Illinois
McLaren, H. J., M.D., Pennsylvania
McLean, Ronald, California
McMurry, Bryce E., M.D., Washington
McQuigg, Ronald W., M.D., Ohio
McQuillan, Marjorie, Washington
Mead, Peyton, M.D., Connecticut
Meerdink, Ellen M., New York
Mella, Barbara A., M.D., Michigan
Mendelsohn, Harvey J., M.D., Ohio
Merz, M. Rosalie, Missouri
Metcalf, Malcolm, Iowa
Mier, Manuel J., M.D., Illinois
Millard, H. D., D.D.S., Michigan
Miller, Allen M., Rev., Pennsylvania
Miller, Alexander, M.D., Ohio
Miller, Barbara, Pennsylvania
Miller, David, M.D., Massachusetts
Miller, Fred C., D.D.S., North Carolina
Miller, John S., M.D., California
Miller, Robert Skeith, M.D., Oregon
Miller, Sam L., M.D., Illinois
Miller, W. Rutledge, M.D., Tennessee
Miller, William W., M.D., California
Millett, John F., D.D.S., New York
Mincks, James, M.D., Iowa
Mirata, Nancy, California
Misuraca, Leroy M., California
Mitchell, Jane A., Ohio
Mitchell, Mancel T., M.D., Minnesota
Monti, M. Jay, Pennsylvania
Monto, Raymond W., M.D., Michigan
Mooney, Cecelia, Oregon
Moore, Robert L., D.D.S., Georgia
Morgan, Dale D., M.D., Iowa
Morgan, Harold W., M.D., Iowa
Morris, Kenneth A., M.D., Florida
Morris, Marlyn Sue, Colorado
Morris, Mary Anna, Arkansas
Morrison, Archie B., D.D.S., Washington
Morrison, Carolyn, New York
Morrison, Mary, California
Morrison, Patricia, Indiana
Morrison, Robert S., M.D., Massachusetts
Morrow, Dorothy, M.D., Vermont
Morrow, Paul L., Vermont

Morrow, Robert Clegg, Vermont
Morrow, Rufus C., M.D., Vermont
Morrow, Sylvia, Indiana
Moss, William, M.D., California
Mount, Lester A., M.D., New York
Mount, Melinda, New York
Mudge, Florence, California
Mueller, Gilbert F., Jr., M.D., Wisconsin
Munchow, Otto B., M.D., California
Munton, Mary, New York
Murphy, Ann M., New York
Murphy, Catherine, Connecticut
Murphy, Eileen, Massachusetts
Murray, Robert W., Virginia
Mussett, Gerald, Colorado
Myers, Philip, M.D., California
Myers, Kermit Whitney, M.D., Iowa
Myers, T. R., M.D., California
Nagel, Harry T., M.D., Illinois
Nash, Henry H., M.D., Washington
Nation, Earl F., M.D., California
Nayden, William A., Rev., Massachusetts
Neal, Richard M., Jr., Tennessee
Needell, Mervin H., M.D., Florida
Neff, Barbara A., Minnesota
Nelson, Marjorie, M.D., Pennsylvania
Netzley, Ralph Edward, M.D., California
Newmark, Franklyn M., M.D., Colorado
Nichols, Ervin F., M.D., California
Nicholson, H., Rev., Ohio
Nixon, Marion M., Canada
Nixon, Robert K., M.D., Michigan
Noble, Andrew, M.D., California
Noorthoek, David J., M.D., California
Norstrom, Shirley Ann, Minnesota
Nosowsky, Emanuel E., M.D., California
Nugent, Janet L., Texas
Nussbaum, Martha J., Tennessee
Nygren, Edward Joseph, M.D., Maryland
O'Bear, Margaret, M.D., New York
Oblender, John, California
O'Brien, Anne, Massachusetts
O'Callaghan. Madeleine, Pennsylvania
O'Connor, Marcella, California
Odekirk, Sharon, Utah
O'Donnell, Geraldine A., California
Ogle, Ben C., Jr., M.D., North Carolina
Oglesby, Daniel, Alabama
Oglesby, Richard B., M.D., Missouri
O'Grady, Roberta S., California
Olen, Else, M.D., Pennsylvania
Oliver, Dalton S., M.D., Louisiana
Olheiser, Kay, Washington
O'Melia, Niall M., District of Columbia
O'Neal, Ruth, M.D., North Carolina
O'Neal, Claire E., New York
Orbeton, Everett A., M.D., Maine
O'Rourke, Thomas, M.D., Oregon
Oslovich, Paul, Rev., C.S.S.R., New York
Owens, Ben P., M.D., Minnesota
Padgett, Darlene, Arizona
Paez, Patricia, Virginia
Palmer, Harriet Jordan, California
Panter, Barry M., M.D., New Jersey
Panter, Mary Lou, New Jersey
Pantera, Robert E., D.D.S., New York
Papegaay, Susan J., New York

Pappas, Gus C., D.D.S., Ohio
Parke, William More, Jr., M.D., New York
Parker, Douglas B., M.D., D.D.S., Florida
Parker, James H., Jr., M.D., Pennsylvania
Parker, Thomas M., M.D., Michigan
Parkinson, Charles E., M.D., Michigan
Parks, Joseph A., M.D., California
Parks, Wilson S., Rev., Indiana
Parmley, Van S., M.D., Kansas
Partlow, Kenneth L., II, M.D., Washington
Pate, Mavis O., Texas
Paul, John R., M.D., District of Columbia
Paulsen, Malcolm, M.D., Vermont
Paulson, Janet Sue, Michigan
Paulus, Carol A., Michigan
Pearlman, Jerome T., M.D., Iowa
Peck, Marie J., Connecticut
Peden, John K., M.D., Wisconsin
Peirce, Christine Joyce, California
Peltier, James R., D.D.S., Louisiana
Pence, Lawrence, M.D., Washington
Pendergrass, Henry, M.D., Massachusetts
Perkins, Roy E., M.D., California
Perloff, Dorothee, M.D., California
Perloff, Philip, M.D., California
Perrett, George, M.D., Iowa
Perry, Elizabeth A., Florida
Perry, Richard E., M.D., Florida
Peters, Ronald G., New York
Peters, William Ralph, New York
Peters, William W., Pennsylvania
Peterson, Robert A., Wisconsin
Petraitis, Dalia, California
Petre, Gail J., Maryland
Pezzlo, Frank, M.D., Connecticut
Philipp, Ernest A., M.D., California
Phillips, Champe E., Texas
Phillips, Eldon W., Illinois
Piatt, Arnold D., M.D., Ohio
Pierce, Esther E., California
Pierson, John C., M.D., Delaware
Pilcher, Mary E., Virginia
Pirkey, Will P., M.D., Colorado
Polachek, Richard S., D.D.S., California
Pollock, Marlene, Michigan
Poppen, Kenneth, M.D., California
Portaro, Marie, West Virginia
Porter, Howard R., M.D., California
Poulton, Roberta, Maryland
Power, R. E., M.D., California
Prendergast, Robert A., M.D., New York
Presberg, Max Howard, M.D., New York
Price, George F., M.D., New York
Price, Robert, Washington
Prince, Stanford, D.D.S., Washington
Proctor, Munro H., M.D., New Hampshire
Pruhsmeier, August W., Oregon
Puchalski, Geraldine, Michigan
Puckett, James F., D.D.S., Texas
Puhl, James Joseph, Iowa
Pulliam, Robert L., Jr., M.D., Washington
Quattlebaum, Frank, M.D., Minnesota
Quattlebaum, Robert B., M.D., Georgia
Quinn, Thomas D., California
Quinn, Winifred A., New York

Raddin, Robin Margot, Virginia
Radley, John B., Rev., C.S.S.R., New York
Radtke, Donna J., Iowa
Ramsden, Charles H., M.D., California
Rapperport, Alan S., M.D., Florida
Ratcliffe, John W., M.D., California
Rawling, John C., M.D., Michigan
Rawnsley, Howard, M.D., Pennsylvania
Read, William A., Maryland
Read, William B., M.D., California
Reaume, Dorothy T., Michigan
Reed, Robert M., D.D.S., Minnesota
Reen, Gertrude A., Massachusetts
Reeves, William A., M.D., California
Reich, Lottie, Arizona
Reid, Frederick K., M.D., New York
Reiley, Richard E., M.D., Minnesota
Reinert, Adelaide T., Illinois
Renehan, Claire A., Rhode Island
Renkwitz, Carol A., New York
Revzin, Marvin E., D.D.S., Michigan
Reyes, Jorge, Ecuador
Rezac, Barbara, Ohio
Rhodes, Winston L., Maryland
Ricci, Henry N., M.D., California
Rich, Mary E., New York
Richards, Jeannette A., M.D., California
Richardson, H. Burtt, Jr., M.D., Maryland
Rickard, Vernon, M.D., California
Ridall, Earle G., M.D., New York
Ries, Roland A., Rev., Maryland
Riffenburgh, Ralph, M.D., California
Riley, Richard L., M.D., California
Rivera, Dorothy, New Jersey
Roach, Charles A., M.D., Minnesota
Robertson, Carole A., California
Robinson, Marsh E., D.D.S., M.D.,
    California
Roden, Ann, Indiana
Rodes, Ned D., M.D., Missouri
Rodgers, Richard S., M.D., Minnesota
Roeber, Renata K., Minnesota
Rogers, Charles S., M.D., Michigan
Rogers, David E., M.D., Tennessee
Rogers, Doris, California
Rogers, S. Perry, M.D., Texas
Rogers, Elise Roberts (Mrs. Walter C.),
    California
Rogers, Walter C., M.D., California
Rohfles, Elaine M., California
Rolf, Bruce B., M.D., California
Romer, William V., Missouri
Romero, Patricia N., Massachusetts
Roppe, Mary Lou, Montana
Rosenbaum, Harold D., M.D., Kentucky
Rosenberg, Barnett, New York
Rosenmann, David E., Pennsylvania
Rosenquist, Charles W., Ohio
Ross, Frederick P., M.D., Massachusetts
Ross, Stanley C., M.D., California
Roth, George J., M.D., California
Roulhac, George E., M.D., Missouri
Rousseau, Barbara, Connecticut
Rowles, Donald F., M.D., California
Rowley, Wm. F., Jr., M.D., Illinois
Royce, Stephen W., M.D., California
Rudeen, Joyce M., Minnesota

Rundles, Walter Z., M.D., Michigan
Rutz, Sharon, Colorado
Ryan, Charles J., M.D., Michigan
Ryan, Robert F., M.D., Louisiana
Rymer, Carol, Colorado
Safer, Jan N., M.D., New York
Sahagian-Edwards, Alex., M.D., New York
Sander, Irvin W., M.D., Michigan
Sandstrom, Susan M., M.D., Texas
Sarno, John E., Jr., M.D., New York
Sasaki, Gordon H., Hawaii
Sasano, Kim, Colorado
Savage, Nancy, Ohio
Savits, Barry S., M.D., New York
Sayers, Martin P., M.D., Ohio
Saypol, George, M.D., New York
Scanlan, David, M.D., New Jersey
Scanlon, George H., M.D., Iowa
Scannell, J. Gordon, M.D., Massachusetts
Schatz, Irwin J., M.D., Michigan
Schenk, Jo Ann, Iowa
Scheverman, Ann, New Hampshire
Schifferli, Marilyn, New Jersey
Schildecker, William, M.D., Florida
Schilke, Joyce, North Carolina
Schlesinger, Martin R., M.D., California
Schmidt, Arthur A., D.D.S., Puerto Rico
Schmidt, Arthur H., D.D.S., Michigan
Schmidt, Jonathan, Michigan
Schmitt, Rosanna, Kentucky
Schoch, Ada C., California
Scholman, John, Jr., M.D., Massachusetts
Schopfer, Madeleine L., Delaware
Schulkins, Thomas, M.D., California
Schutz, Joseph A., M.D., New York
Schwartz, Robert J., Washington
Schwenk, Barbara, North Dakota
Seagrave, Kenneth H., M.D., New York
Seaman, William, Massachusetts
Sears, W. Norman, M.D., California
Secor, Nicholas T., New York
Seeley, Esther, Massachusetts
Segerberg, Ludwig, M.D., Kentucky
Seidel, Henry M., M.D., Maryland
Seipel, Harriet J., California
Sell, Harold H., D.D.S., Michigan
Sell, L. Stanley, M.D., Idaho
Sellig, Robert, Vermont
Selvaratnam, Indran, Tennessee
Selverstone, Bertram, M.D.,
    Massachusetts
Selzer, Jane, M.D., California
Seminario, Alfredo, M.D., Florida
Serrano, Francisco S., Texas
Sexton, Margaret, New Jersey
Shanley, Susan K., Maryland
Shaw, Anthony, M.D., New York
Shaw, Cynthia C., District of Columbia
Shaw, Judith Anne, Massachusetts
Shaw, Robert R., M.D., Texas
Shedd, Donald P., M.D., Connecticut
Sheil, Eileen Patricia, District of
    Columbia
Shepherd, R. W., M.D., Canada
Sherman, Ann, New York
Sherman, John J., Virginia
Sherwood, Margaret, Ohio

Shocket, Everett, M.D., Florida
Shooshan, Harry M., Maryland
Shrifter, Norman W., M.D., California
Sicks, Mary E., Illinois
Sidell, Chester M., M.D., California
Simmons, Donald R., M.D., Michigan
Sinclair, Dolores, California
Singerman, Leonard J., M.D., Kentucky
Sisler, David A., M.D., California
Sister Charles Marie Frank, District of
  Columbia
Sizer, Elvira, Michigan
Skeels, Robert F., M.D., California
Skiles, James H., Jr., M.D., Illinois
Slining, Judy M., Michigan
Small, Irwin A., D.D.S., Michigan
Smith, Byron, M.D., New York
Smith, Elizabeth Ann, Virginia
Smith, Janice J., California
Smith, Ransan L., M.D., Washington
Smith, Robert G., M.D., Ohio
Smith, Suzanne L., New Jersey
Smith, Veronica, Pennsylvania
Smoller, Arnold J., M.D., New York
Snow, Donald L., Maryland
Snow, L. B., M.D., North Carolina
Snyder, Howard M., III, Massachusetts
Snyder, Joseph F., Jr., D.D.S., Florida
Sobeck, Frederick J., M.D., California
Sommer, W. Paul, D.D.S., Oklahoma
Sontos, Alexander, New Jersey
Soto, Ana Gloria, Ph.D., Florida
Soule, Dolores M., North Carolina
Soule, Elizabeth, North Carolina
Southwick, Wayne O., M.D.,
  Connecticut
Spangler, Paul E., M.D., California
Spar, Arthur A., M.D., California
Spence, Mary A., Ohio
Sperelakis, Nick, Ph.D., Ohio
Spino, Pascal Daniel, M.D., Pennsylvania
Spock, Alexander, M.D., North Carolina
Spofford, Andrew, Idaho
Spofford, William B., Jr., Rev., Idaho
Spreckelmyer, Marylouise, Indiana
Springer, Joe P., M.D., Wisconsin
Spruill, Leon, Maryland
Staatz, Dumont S., M.D., Washington
Stack, Robert E., M.D., Minnesota
Stafford, C. E., M.D., California
Stafford, Diana R., Washington
Stanley, Mildred, M.D., New York
Stanziola, Mary E., Pennsylvania
Staples, Albert F., D.M.D., Texas
Stark, Marvin Michael, D.D.S., California
Steadman, Rodger C., Pennsylvania
Steele, Jeffrey L., District of Columbia
Steffen, Elizabeth A., M.D., Wisconsin
Stein, Barbara B., M.D., Ohio
Steiner, Joan M., Kansas
Stern, C. A., M.D., South Dakota
Stevens, Alexander R., Jr., M.D.,
  Washington
Stevenson, Thomas C., M.D., California
Stevenson, William D., M.D., Canada
Stewart, H. C., M.D., Nebraska
Stewart, John E., M.D., Washington

Stocker, Harold H., M.D., California
Stocker, William B., D.D.S., Missouri
Stokley, Sam P. H., M.D., Florida
Stoll, Carolyn, Michigan
Storkan, Margaret Ann, M.D., California
Storms, William W., Wisconsin
Straub, Daniel L., M.D., California
Straub, Margaret E., California
Strauss, Arnold, M.D., Virginia
Striker, Cecil, M.D., Ohio
Stringer, Barbara, Michigan
Strong, Caroline L., Maryland
Strong, Priscilla, Massachusetts
Stubenbord, John, M.D., New York
Stump, Charles A., M.D., Florida
Strum, Carol A., Ohio
Sullivan, Martha I., Minnesota
Swackhamer, William D., M.D., Nevada
Sweet, Patricia, Massachusetts
Swendson, James J., M.D., Minnesota
Taber, Rodman E., M.D., Michigan
Tank, Gerhard, M.D., Oregon
Tarcher, Alyce Bezman, M.D., California
Taren, James A., M.D., Michigan
Tatlock, Hugh, M.D., Massachusetts
Tegenkamp, Irene E., Ohio
Templeton, Richard K., Maryland
Territo, Mary Carol, Michigan
Terry, John L., M.D., Ohio
Tetirick, Jack E., M.D., Ohio
Thal, Sam H., M.D., California
Thomas, Anhurd, D.D.S., Connecticut
Thomas, Merle, M.D., Texas
Thomas, Wm. N., Jr., M.D., Maryland
Thompson, Anne, North Carolina
Thompson, Arthur F., M.D., California
Thompson, J. Daniel, M.D., Georgia
Thompson, Jack E., M.D., California
Thompson, John B., M.D., Georgia
Thompson, Raymond K., M.D., Maryland
Thompson, Richard C., M.D., California
Thornton, Margene, Iowa
Thorson, Cleo J., Michigan
Till, Harry J., M.D., Alabama
Tilney, Robt. W., Jr., M.D., New Jersey
Timmons, Elizabeth F., Maine
Tisher, Paul W., M.D., Connecticut
Tocantins, Ronald, M.D., Washington
Torres, Fernando, M.D., Minnesota
Toth, Robert J., New York
Tremblay, Louise, New Hampshire
Troland, Charles E., M.D., Virginia
Trowbridge, Frederick L., Ohio
Tucker, Charles E., M.P.H., Kentucky
Tucker, Grace, Massachusetts
Turner, Paralee A., Washington
Turner, Thomas A., M.D., Kansas
Twaler, Mary F., Illinois
Twedt, Nancy E., Minnesota
Tyrer, A. Roy, Jr., M.D., Tennessee
Underwood, Rex J., M.D., Oregon
Utne, J. Richard, M.D., Iowa
Vande Bunte, Ethel, Michigan
Vandenberg, Henry, Jr., M.D., Michigan
Vandergriff, Katherine, Tennessee
Van Haitsma, Phyllis, Iowa
Van Raalte, Leslie, Massachusetts

Vaughn, Edith E., Tennessee
Vedder, J. S., M.D., Wisconsin
Versic, Thomas, M.D., Ohio
Vescovi, Barbara D., New York
Vettoretti, Johana O., New York
Vickers, James Edmund, M.D., California
Villegas, Oscar, D.D.S., Michigan
Visser, J. Hugh, M.D., California
Voltz, Vernon C., M.D., Illinois
Voss, Henry S., Rev., Pennsylvania
Vyn Meier, William, Michigan
Waggoner, Jeffrey Robert, Colorado
Waite, Daniel, D.D.S., Minnesota
Walker, James C., M.D., Massachusetts
Walker, Philip H., M.D., Massachusetts
Walker, Rebecca M., Oklahoma
Wall, D. D., M.D., Texas
Wallace, Evelyn G., M.D., California
Waller, John T., M.D., Kansas
Walsh, Edmund N., M.D., Texas
Walsh, John T., Maryland
Walsh, John W., M.D.,
  District of Columbia
Walsh, Thomas S., Maryland
Walsh, William B., M.D., Maryland
Walsh, Wm. B., Jr., Maryland
Ward, Helen, North Carolina
Ward, Jennie, Washington
Warner, Willis A., M.D., Iowa
Waterman, David, M.D., Tennessee
Watkins, Anne, M.D., California
Watkins, Beverly, P., Virginia
Watkins, Melvin B., M.D., New York
Wavernek, Mary C., Wisconsin
Wawro, N., Williams, M.D., Connecticut
Wayne, J. Paul, M.D., California
Weatherford, Rosalie, Virginia
Weaver, Donald G., Iowa
Weaver, Philip, M.D., Colorado
Weaver, Samuel, M.D., California
Webb, Dean I., D.D.S., Oregon
Webb, Gilbert A., M.D., California
Webb, Richard F., M.D., California
Weber, Maurice, Florida
Webster, Dorothy, Massachusetts
Weed, Chester A., M.D., Connecticut
Weed, Jeffrey Floyd, Connecticut
Weeter, John C., M.D., Kentucky
Weeter, John M., Kentucky
Wehrle, Julie Ann, Pennsylvania
Weinschreider, Mary, Michigan
Weisman, Lawrence D., Ohio
Weisskopf, Alex, M.D., California
Welch, Ilse D., California
Weller, Harriet V., Illinois
Weller, Lorraine, Missouri
Weller, Wm. J., M.D., California
Wenaas, Elmer J., M.D., Ohio
Wertz, Myrtle, Virginia
Wessel, Hazel E., Hawaii
Westcott, F. Howard, M.D., New Jersey

Westcott, Georgia, New Jersey
Westerman, Richard L., M.D., Indiana
Whalen, Thomas, New York
Whelan, Raymond, Rev., New York
Whelton, James A., M.D., Massachusetts
Whittington, Betty, California
Wieczorowski, Elsie, M.D., Illinois
Wiener, Morris F., M.D., New York
Wier, Marion E., M.D., Massachusetts
Wiggins, Nellie, Florida
Wilcox, John C., M.D., California
Wild, Lois Ann, New Jersey
Wilhelm, John, Illinois
Willard, James D., Colorado
Williams, John E., M.D., Washington
Williams, Kathleen, Washington
Williams, Kenneth O., M.D., California
Williamson, William P., M.D., Kansas
Wilson, Katherine B.,
  District of Columbia
Windust, James R., Washington
Winter, Doris, Pennsylvania
Wise, James K., M.D., Colorado
Wochos, Robert G., M.D., Wisconsin
Wohlgemuth, Joan, M.D.,
  District of Columbia
Wolkin, Julius, M.D., Ohio
Wollman, Edward L., California
Wood, Judith Lee, M.D., Illinois
Wood, T. Rodman, M.D., California
Woodruff, Stephen, Georgia
Woods, Francis M., M.D., Massachusetts
Woodward, Charles M., D.D.S., California
Woodward, Sarah, South Carolina
Wright, Carleton James, M.D., California
Wright, Charles Howard, M.D., Michigan
Wright, Donald, Wyoming
Wright, John J., M.D., North Carolina
Wrobleski, Helen M., Massachusetts
Wyatt, William M., M.D., Georgia
Yankee, Ronald A., M.D.,
  District of Columbia
Yates, Basil, M.D., Florida
Yates, James E., M.D., California
Yeager, Henry, Jr., M.D., Texas
Youker, James, M.D., Virginia
Young, Forrest, M.D., California
Young, G. Victoria, M.D., California
Young, Malcolm C., M.D., Michigan
Yount, Billy G., Jr., Oklahoma
Zane, Letty Lou, California
Zecchino, V., M.D., Rhode Island
Zeier, Francis G., M.D., Indiana
Zeier, Olga G., Indiana
Zenick, Alice Valentina, Connecticut
Zimmer, Walter W., Rev., Ohio
Zink, Rosemary E., Pennsylvania
Zimmerman, Bernard, M.D.,
  West Virginia
Zimmerman, George R., M.D., Iowa